Shakuntala Devi's
Book of Numbers

CW00386319

Everything You Always W
But was Difficult to Under

We can't live without numbers. We need them in our daily chores, big and small. But we carry in us a certain fear of numbers and are never confident about using them. Shakuntala Devi, the internationally famous mathematical wizard, makes it easy for us— and interesting.

This book contains all we always wanted to know about numbers but was difficult to understand, and which was nowhere available. Divided into three parts, the first will tell you everything about numbers, the second some anecdotes related with numbers and mathematicians, and the third a few important tables that will always help you.

Shakuntala Devi popularly known as "the human computer." is a world famous mathematical prodigy who continues to outcompute the most sophisticated computers. She took only fifty seconds to calculate the twenty-third root of a 201 digit number. To verify her answer, a computer in Washington programmed with over 13,000 instructions took ten seconds longer. Shakuntala Devi firmly believes that mathematics can be great fun for everybody.

"... makes very. interesting reading and provides valuable information."

Hindu

Shakuntala Devi's
BOOK
OF
NUMBERS

**Everything You Always Wanted to Know About Numbers
But Was Difficult to Understand**

Orient
Paperbacks

DELHI | MUMBAI | HYDERABAD

"And Lucy, dear child, mind your arithmetic... what would life be without arithmetic, but a scene of horrors?"

- Sydney Smith

www.orientpaperbacks.com

ISBN 81-222-0006-0

1st Published 1984
26th Printing 2004

The Book of Numbers: Everything you always wanted to know about numbers but was difficult to understand

© Shakuntala Devi

Cover design by Vision Studio

Published by
Orient Paperbacks
(A division of Vision Books Pvt. Ltd.)
Madarsa Road, Kashmere Gate, Delhi-110 006

Printed in India at
Rashtra Rachna Printers, Delhi-110 092

Cover Printed at
Ravindra Printing Press, Delhi-110 006

CONTENTS

AUTHOR'S NOTE

Many go through life afraid of numbers and upset by numbers. They would rather amble along through life miscounting, miscalculating and in general mismanaging their worldly affairs than make friends with numbers. The very word 'numbers' scares most people. They'd rather not know about it. And asking questions about numbers would only make them look ignorant and unintelligent. Therefore they decide to take the easy way out--not have anything to do with numbers.

But numbers rule our lives. We use numbers all the time throughout the day. The year, month and date on which we are living is a number. The time of the day is a number. The time of our next appointment is again a number. And the money we earn and spend is also a number. There is no way we can live our lives dispensing with numbers.

Knowing more about numbers and being acquainted with them will not only enrich our lives, but also contribute towards managing our day to day affairs much better.

This book is designed to give you that basic information about numbers, that will take away the scare of numbers out of your mind.

EVERYTHING ABOUT NUMBERS

1
WHAT IS A NUMBER ?

A number is actually a way of thinking, an idea, that enables us to compare very different sets of objects. It can actually be called an idea behind the act of counting.

2
WHAT ARE NUMERALS ?

Numerals are used to name numbers, in other words, a numeral is a symbol used to represent a number. For example, the numeral 4 is the name of number four. And again four is the idea that describes any collection of four objects. 4 marbles, 4 books, 4 people, 4 colours, and so on. We recognize that these collections all have the quality of 'fourness' even though they may differ in every other way.

3
WHAT ARE DIGITS ?

Digits are actually the alphabets of numbers. Just as we use the twenty-six letters of the alphabet to build words, we use the ten digits 0, 1, 2, 3, 4, 5, 6, 7, 8, and 9 to build numerals.

4

IS 10 A DIGIT ?

No. 10 is a numeral formed from the two digits 1 and 0.

5

WHAT IS THE COMMONLY USED BASIS OF OUR NUMBER SYSTEM ?

The commonly used basis of our system of numeration is grouping into sets of ten or multiples of ten.

6

HOW ARE NUMBERS TRANSLATED INTO WORDS ?

Any number, however large it may be, given in numerical form may be translated into words by using the following form :

and so on	Hundred Millions	Ten Millions	Millions	Hundred Thousands	Ten Thousands	Thousands	Hundreds	Tens	Ones

Thus the number 458, 386, 941 can be expressed in words as 'Four hundred fifty eight million, three hundred eighty six thousand, nine hundred forty one.

7

IS IT ALRIGHT TO CALL $3+2$ 'THREE AND TWO'?

No. $3+2$ is always called 'Three plus two'. There is no arithmetical operation called 'and'.

8

WHAT ARE THE DIFFERENT TYPES OF NUMERALS USED IN DAY-TO-DAY LIFE ?

Besides our own number system, known as the Hindu-Arabic system, the Roman numerals are also used sometimes. They are occasionally seen in text books, clock faces and building inscriptions.

9

WHAT IS THE ORIGIN OF ROMAN NUMERALS AND HOW ACTUALLY IS THE COUNTING DONE IN THIS SYSTEM ?

Roman numerals originated in Rome and were used by the ancient Romans almost 2,000 years ago. In this system seven symbols are used :

I   V   X   L   C   D   M

The numbers represented are 1, 5 and multiples of 5 and 10, the number of fingers on one hand and on two hands. There is no zero in this system. The other numerals like 2, 3, 6 are represented with these above symbols by placing them in a row and adding or subtracting, such as :

1 = I   6 = VI (V+I)
2 = II   7 = VII (V+I+I)
3 = III   8 = VIII (V+I+I+I)
4 = IV (one subtracted   9 = IX (1 subtracted
         from five)   from X)
5 = V   10 = X

19 = XIX;   27 = XXVII; 152 = CLII
                   and so on.

Roman numerals were used by bankers and book-keepers until the eighteenth century as they did not trust symbols like 6, 8 or 9 that could easily be changed to other numbers by a dishonest accountant

10

WHERE DID OUR OWN NUMBER SYSTEM ORIGINATE ?

Our present numerals known as the Hindu-Arabic numerals is said to have originated from the Arabs, Persians, Egyptians and Hindus. It is presumed

12

that the intercourse among traders served to carry the symbols from country to country, and therefore a conglomeration from the four different sources.

However, the country which first used the largest number of numeral forms is said to be India.

11
WHERE DID THE CONCEPT OF ZERO ORIGINATE ?

The concept of zero is attributed to the Hindus. The Hindus were also the first to use zero in the way it is used today. Some symbol was required in positional number systems to mark the place of a power of the base not actually occurring. This was indicated by the Hindus by a small circle, which was called 'Sunya', the Sanskrit word for vacant. This was translated into the Arabic 'Sifr' about 800 A.D. Subsequent changes have given us the word zero.

12
IS IT BAD TO COUNT ON THE FINGERS ?

No. Not really. It is slow and it can also be in-convenient, but it is the natural way to start, it is very useful in memorising one digit additions.

13

WHAT ARE CARDINAL NUMBERS AND ORDINAL NUMBERS ?

An ordinal number gives us the rank or order of a particular object and the cardinal number states how many objects are in the group of collection. To quote an example, 'fifth' is an ordinal number and 'five' is a cardinal number.

14

WHERE DO THE + AND — SIGNS COME FROM!

The + symbol came from the Latin word 'et' meaning and. The two symbols were used in the fifteenth century to show that boxes of merchandise were overweight or underweight. For overweight they used the sign + and for underweight the sign — . Within about 40 years accountants and mathematicians started using them,

15

WHERE DID THE ÷ SIGN COME FROM ?

The fraction $\frac{2}{3}$ means two divided by 3, and ÷ looks like a fraction.

16
WHO DISCOVERED THE SYMBOL = FOR EQUALS!

Robert Recorde, the mathematician, invented it in 1557. He decided that two equal length parallel lines were as equal as anything available.

17
WHAT ARE PERFECT NUMBERS AND AMICABLE OR SYMPATHETIC NUMBERS ?

A perfect number can be described as an integer which is equal to the sum of all its factors except itself. For example, the number 28 is a perfect number since

$$28 = 1 + 2 + 4 + 7 + 14$$

Amicable or sympathetic are two numbers each of which is equal to the sum of all the exact divisors of the other except the number itself. For example, 220 and 224 are amicable numbers for 220 has the exact divisors 1, 2, 4, 5, 10, 11, 20, 22, 44, 55 and 110, whose sum is 284 and 284 has the exact divisors 1, 2, 4, 71 and 142 whose sum is 220.

18
WHAT SIGN IS 0, + OR — SIGN ?

Neither. Zero is not a sign at all, because adding

and subtracting it changes nothing. Multiplying by it gives zero and dividing by it is not allowed at all.

19
HOW WOULD YOU DESCRIBE PRIME NUMBERS AND COMPOSITE NUMBERS ?

An integer can be called a prime number when it has no integral factors except unity and itself, such as 2, 3, 5, 7, 11, or 13. And numbers which have factors such as 9, 15, 25, 32 are composite numbers. About twenty-two centuries ago, a Greek geographer-astronomer named Erastosthenes used a sieve for sifting the composite numbers out of the natural numbers. Those remaining, of course, are prime numbers.

20
HOW WOULD YOU DESCRIBE THE SIEVE OF ERASTOSTHENES ?

The most effective known method of locating primes, this procedure separates the primes out of the set of all whole numbers.

The whole numbers are arranged in six columns starting with two, as shown. Then the primes are circled and all multiples of 2 are crossed out. Next the number 3 is circled and all the multiples of 3 are crossed out. Next the same thing is done to 5 and 7. The circled numbers remaining are the primes.

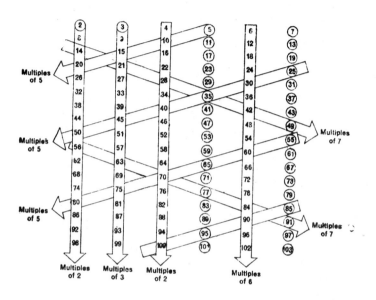

21
WHY DO THEY CALL IT A SIEVE ?

Mathematicians call this procedure a SIEVE because it is a way of filtering the primes from the other whole numbers.

22
WHY ISN'T ONE A PRIME NUMBER ?

If one is allowed as a prime, then any number could be written as a product of primes in many ways. For example :

$$12 = 1 \times 2 \times 2 \times 3$$
$$\text{or } 12 = 1 \times 1 \times 2 \times 2 \times 3$$
$$\text{or } 12 = 1 \times 1 \times 1 \times 1 \times 1 \times 2 \times 2 \times 3$$

The fact that factoring into primes can only be done in one way is important in mathematics.

23
HOW DID THE WORD 'PRIME' FOR PRIME NUMBERS ORIGINATE ?

It originates from the Latin word 'primus', meaning first in importance. Primes are the important main ingredient of numbers, for every number is either a prime or a product of primes.

24
WHAT IS A PRIME-FACTOR ?

A prime number that is a factor of another number is called a prime factor of the number. For example, the number 24 can be expressed as a product of its prime factors in three ways:

24	24	24
3×8	4×6	2×12

24	24	24
3×8	4×6	2×12
3×2×4	2×2×3×2	2×3×4
3×2×2×2		2×3×2×2

∴   24= 2×2×2×3

25

WHAT IS A FACTOR TREE ?

Factor tree is a very helpful way to think about fractions. For example, if we want to take out the factors of 1764 here is the way to go about it :

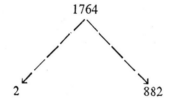

First we divide by the smallest prime, which is 2. 1764÷2 = 882. We write down the 2 and the quotient 882.

Then we divide the quotient 882 by 2 again. 882 ÷ 2 = 441. On a new row we write down both 2's and the quotient 441.

Next, since 441, the last quotient cannot be any longer divided by 2, we divide it by the next prime number 3, continue so on, and stop when we at last find a prime quotient. In the end the tree should look like this—

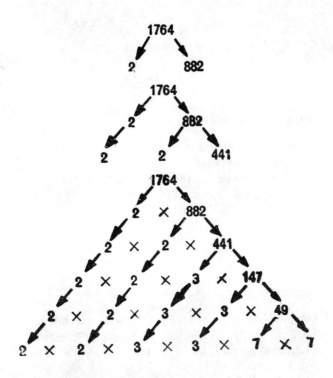

$$1764 = 2 \times 2 \times 3 \times 3 \times 7 \times 7 = 2^2 \times 3^2 \times 7^2$$

You will note that at each level of the tree the product of the horizontal numbers is equal to the original number to be factored.

The last row, of course, gives the prime factors.

26
WHY IS IT THAT ANY NUMBER RAISED TO THE POWER ZERO IS EQUAL TO 1 AND NOT ZERO ?

The answer is very simple. When we raise a number to the power 0, we are not actually multiplying the particular number by 0. For example, let us take 2^0. In this case we are not actually multiplying the number 2 by 0.

We define $2^0 = 1$, so that each power of 2 is one factor of 2 larger than the last, e.g., 1, 2, 4, 8, 16, 32 . . .

27
WHAT IS THE DIFFERENCE BETWEEN ALGORITHM AND LOGARITHM ?

Algorithm is a noun meaning some special process of solving a certain type of problem. Whereas logarithm, again a noun, is the exponent of that power of a fixed number, called the base, which equals a given number, called the antilogarithm.
In 10 = 100, 10 is the base, 2 is the logarithm and 100 the antilogarithm.

28
WHAT IS SO 'NATURAL' ABOUT NATURAL NUMBERS ?

Natural numbers are positive integers, in other words whole numbers which may be cardinal numbers or ordinal numbers.

29
THEN WHAT ARE UNNATURAL NUMBERS. ?

There is no such term called unnatural numbers, but there is a term called negative numbers. The introduction of negative numbers is due to the need for subtraction to be performable without restriction. In the case of positive numbers the subtraction $a - b = c$ can only be carried out if a is greater than b. If, on the other hand, a is smaller than b we define $c = - (b-a)$, for example $7-9 = (-2)$. Here the '— sign' on the left hand side of the equation represents an operation, and on the right hand side it forms part of the number itself. In the case of the positive numbers the associated sign $+$ may be omitted, but such is not the case with negative numbers.

30
WHAT IS A MANIAC ?

MANIAC is an acronym for Mathematical Analyzer, Numerical Integrator and Computer.

It is an automatic digital computing machine at the Los Alamos Scientific Laboratory.

31
WHAT IS AN ARITHMOMETER ?

It is a computing machine.

32
WHAT IS DUO-DECIMAL SYSTEM OF NUMBERS ?

It is a system of numbers in which twelve is the base instead of ten. For example, in DUODECIMAL system 24 would mean two twelves plus four, which would be 28 in the decimal system.

33
WHAT IS EDVAC ?

It is a computing machine built at the University of Pennsylvania for the Ballistic Research Laboratories, Aberdeen Proving ground. EDVAC is an acronym for ELECTRONIC DESCRETE VARIABLE AUTOMATIC COMPUTER.

34
WHAT IS AN EXPONENT ?

The exponent is a number placed at the right of

and above a symbol. The value assigned to the symbol, with this exponent is called a *power* of the symbol; although power is sometimes used in the same sense as exponent. For example, $a^4 = a \times a \times a \times a$ or a multiplied by itself four times. In this case the exponent is 4.

Exponent is also known as the INDEX.

If the exponent is a positive integer, it indicates that the symbol is to be taken as a factor as many times as there are units in this integer. However, when the exponent is negative, it indicates that in addition to operation indicated by the numerical value of the exponent, the quantity is to be reciprocated. For example:

$$3^{-2} = (9)^{-1} = \tfrac{1}{9} \text{ or } 3^{-2} = (3^{-1})^2 = \sqrt{\tfrac{1}{9}} = \tfrac{1}{3}$$

35

WHAT IS A FAREY SEQUENCE ?

The Farey Sequence of order n is the increasing of all fractions P/q for which $0 \leqq p/q \leqq 1, q \leqq N$, and p and q are non-negative integers with no common divisors other than 1. For example, the Farey Sequence of order 5 is:

$$\tfrac{0}{1}, \ \tfrac{1}{5}, \ \tfrac{1}{4}, \ \tfrac{1}{3}, \ \tfrac{2}{5}, \ \tfrac{1}{2}, \ \tfrac{3}{5}, \ \tfrac{2}{3}, \ \tfrac{3}{4}, \ \tfrac{4}{5}, \ \tfrac{1}{1}$$

36
WHAT IS FIBONACCI SEQUENCE ?

The sequence of numbers 1, 1, 2, 3, 5, 8, 13, 21, 34 . . . . each of which sum is the sum of the two previous numbers. These numbers are also called Fibonacci numbers. The ratio of one Fibonacci to the preceding one is a Convergent of the continued fraction:

$$1 + \frac{1}{1} + \frac{1}{1} + \frac{1}{1} + \frac{1}{1} + \cdots$$

The sum of the Fibonacci Sequence can be directly obtained from Pascal's triangle given below:

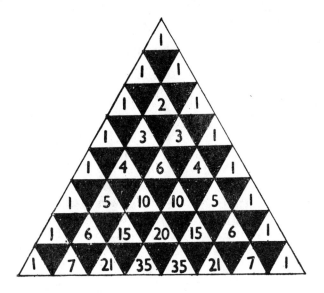

37
WHAT IS PASCAL'S TRIANGLE ?

This is a triangular array of numbers composed of the coefficients of the expansion of $(a+b)^n$, $n = 0$, 1, 2, 3 etc.

Each sum of the slant diagonal is a Fibonacci number. The consecutive sums are 1, 1, 2, 3, 5, 8, 13, 21, 34, 55.

38
WHAT IS PARENTHESES ?

Parentheses is the symbol ( ), indicating that the enclosed sums or products are to be taken collectively.

$2(6+4-3) = 2 \times 7 = 14$

39
WHAT IS PARITY ?

When two integers are both odd or both even they are said to have the same parity. However if one is odd and the other even, then they are said to have different parity.

40
WHAT IS A FINITE SERIES ?

Finite series is a series that terminates at some assigned term.

41
AND WHAT IS INFINITE SERIES ?

Infinite series is a series with an unlimited number of series.

42
WHAT IS AN ARITHMETIC SEQUENCE ?

An arithmetic sequence is a sequence of numbers in which two consecutive terms always have the same difference.

43
IN WHAT WAY DOES ARITHMETIC SEQUENCE DIFFER FROM ARITHMETIC SERIES ?

The Arithmetic Series is actually the unevaluated sum of terms of an arithmetic sequence.

44
WHAT IS ABSCISSA ?

Abscissa means the measure meant to a point from the zero point. Or it can also be the point of intersection of the coordinate lines in graphs or analytical geometry, the measurement being along the horizontal axis, usually called the X axis.

45
WHAT ARE ABSTRACT NUMBERS ?

They are numbers used without connection to any particular object as — 3, 8, 2. But when these numbers are applied to anything as 3 apples, 8 men, 2 cars, they become concrete numbers.

46
IS IT ALRIGHT TO CALL $\frac{12}{4}$, AS 'TWELVE OVER FOUR ?

No. It's a division and it is best to call it 'twelve divided by four'?

47
WHY DO WE SUBTRACT IN THE DIVISION PROCESS ?

Division is actually a repeated subtraction. When

you divide 80 from any number, you are actually subtracting 8 ten times. Division is only a quicker way of subtracting.

48
WHAT ARE ALIQUOT PARTS ?

Aliquot is actually a part of a number or quantity which will divide the number or quantity without a remainder. It can also be called a submultiple. For example 4 is an Aliquot or submultiple of 16.

49
HOW DID THE SIGN √ FOR ROOTS ORIGINATE ?

The word root originates from the word *radix* in Latin. Around 1525 they began to abbreviate it with the letter ȣ in handwriting. Soon γ led to —to γ to √

50
WHAT IS ANTECEDENT IN THE LANGUAGE OF ARITHMETIC ?

Antecedent is the first two terms of a ratio. Thus in the ratio of 3 to 4 written 3:4 the term 3 is the antecedent. It is also the first and third terms of a proportion. Thus 3:4 : :5:6, 3 and 5 are the antecedents and 4 and 6 are the consequents.

51

WHAT ARE 'RAGGED DECIMALS ?

Ragged decimals are those that have varying numbers of digits to the right of the decimal point. Here is an example of the addition of ragged decimals:

$$
\begin{array}{r}
3.62 \\
57.837 \\
4.96 \\
.0043 \\
\hline
66.4213 \\
\hline
\end{array}
$$

52

WHAT IS AN EQUIVALENT FRACTION ?

Fractions that have the same value but are written differently are equivalent.
For example:

$$1\tfrac{1}{4} = \tfrac{5}{2} = \tfrac{10}{4} = \tfrac{20}{8}\ldots$$

are equivalent.

53

WHAT DOES 'ONE DECIMAL PLACE' MEAN ?

It means one digit to the right of the decimal point. For example, 3.5 has one decimal digit, 3.53 has two decimal digits and so on.

54
WHAT ARE SIGNED NUMBERS?

Signed numbers are actually a book keeping concept which were used in book-keeping by the ancient Greeks, Chinese and Hindus more than 2,000 years ago. Merchants wrote positive numbers in black and negative numbers in red in their account books. Many banks still use red to show negative credit.

55
WHAT IS 'ARBITRARY' ?

In Arithmetic Arbitrary means not governed by any fixed rule or standard—chosen according to one's own will.

56
WHAT IS 'REPEATING DECIMAL' ?

A repeating decimal is one in which some sequence of digits is endlessly repeated.

For example:

$0.333 = .\overline{3}$ and $0.272727 = 0.\overline{27}$

are repeating decimals. The bar over the number is a shorthand way of showing those numbers are repeated.

57

WHAT IS 'ARITHMETICAL MEAN' ?

The Arithmetical Mean of any number of quantities is the sum of those quantities divided by their number. It can be called the sum of any number of consecutive terms of an Arithmetical Progression divided by the terms taken.

58

WHERE DOES THE PHRASE 'PERCENT' COME FROM ?

PERCENT comes from the Latin words PER CENTUM meaning 'by the hundred' or 'for every hundred'. The number expressed as a percent is being compared with a second number called the standard or BASE by dividing the base into 100 equal parts and writing the comparison number as so many hundredths of the base.

59

DOES 'OF' ALWAYS MEAN MULTIPLY ?

It can mean many things. However, when it is used in percent problems, it always means a multiplication is coming up.

60
HOW DID THE SYMBOL ' % 'ORIGINATE ?

The symbol '%' means '100'. It started as 100 then 1oo, then $\frac{0}{0}$ in the 17th century and finally 0/0 or %.

61
CAN WE PERFORM THE FOUR OPERATIONS OF ADD, SUBTRACT, MULTIPLY AND DIVIDE PERCENT NUMBERS ?

No, you cannot. Percent only helps you to compare two numbers, and so it cannot be used in the normal arithmetic operations. There always has to be some reference or base given in order for the percent number to have any meaning at all.

62
WHAT IS THE PRACTICAL USE OF PERCENT CALCULATIONS ?

The practical use of Percent is in the calculation of a part or percentage of some total. Here are some typical of practical problems that can be solved by percent calculations:

(a) Supposing a door to door sales person is paid 12% commission on all sales, how much does he earn on a total sale of £ 500·00 ?

(b) The list price of a motor car is £ 3,298/-. On a special sale it is offered at a discount of 20%. What is the sale price ?

(c) Supposing you borrow £300 and the bank specifies that you repay it at £ 30 per month plus interest at 6% per month on the unpaid balance what interest do you actually pay ?

63

WHAT IS 'CHANGE OF SIGNS' ?

If a bracket is preceded by a minus sign then all the signs inside a bracket change from—to + or + to— when the bracket is removed. A plus sign in front of a bracket causes no change of sign inside the bracket when it is removed. For example :

—(6—2+3) becomes —6+2—3 but +(3—4—8) remains 3— 4— 8. When there is no sign of + or— in front of a term, it can always be assumed as a plus term.

64

WHAT IS 'CONVERGENT SERIES' ?

An infinite series is said to be convergent when the sum of the first n terms cannot exceed some finite quantity numerically, no matter how great n may be.

65
AND WHAT IS 'DIVERGENT SERIES' ?

On the other hand, Divergent series is one the sum of whose first n terms either increases indefinitely or oscillates indefinitely between finite limits, as n increases indefinitely.

66
WHAT IS 'CROSS-MULTIPLICATION' ?

When you multiply the numerator on one side of an equation, by the denominator on the other side of the equation, cross multiplication takes place. This operation is carried out for both sides of an equation in order to eliminate fractions.

67
HOW CAN ONE REMEMBER WHICH IS THE NUMERATOR AND WHICH IS THE DENOMINATOR ?

The way to remember it would be Denominator is the down part. D for down.

68
WHAT ARE 'CUMULATIVE SYMBOLS' ?

They are marks or signs ($\times$) meaning multiplied by or ($\div$) meaning divided by.

69
WHEN YOU SAY 'DEDUCE' IN ARITHMETIC, WHAT ACTUALLY DO YOU MEAN ?

Deduce actually means to infer something from information obtained. In other words, to derive or draw a conclusion by reasoning from given principles.

70
HOW DOES 'DEDUCE' RELATE TO DEDUCTION ?

Deduction is a noun derived from the verb 'Deduct'. If derived from Deduce it means to infer, to draw conclusions by reasoning from given principles. To sieve out all the unnecessary information from a problem and draw out the plain facts.

However, when this word is derived from Deduct, it means subtracting or taking away.

71
WHAT IS 'BINARY SYSTEM' OF ARITHMETIC ?

Binary means consisting of two parts or things. The Binary number system is actually a system of notation which uses the base 2 combined with place value of notation. Since the scale is 2, there are only two digits or 'bigits' 0 and 1. If there is one more than 1, we turn from the unit's place to the two's place, thus

$$1+1 = 10$$

To convert any number such as 31 (scale 10) to scale 2, repeated division by 2 is necessary.

$$31 \div 2 = 15\,R1$$
$$15 \div 2 = 7\,R1$$
$$7 \div 2 = 3\,R1$$
$$3 \div 2 = 1\,R1$$

Therefore 31 (Scale 10) = $(1 \times 2^4) + (1 \times 2^3)\ (1 \times 2^2)$ $+ (1 \times 2) + (1 \times 1) = 11,111$ in scale 2.

BASE 10	BINARY SYSTEM
1	1
2	10
3	11
4	100
5	101
6	110
7	111
8	1,000
9	1,001
10	1,010
11	1,011
12	1,100
13	1,101
14	1,110
15	1,111
16	10,000
17	10,001
18	10,010
19	10,011
20	10,100

72

WHAT USE IS THE BINARY SYSTEM IN MODERN WORLD ?

The main use of the Binary System, is its usefulness in electronic computing machines. When an electric circuit is open, in other words, when there is no current, the situation may be regarded as signifying 0. A closed circuit signifies 1.

73

WHAT IS 'PLACE VALUE' ?

The common scale of notation we use in our day-to-day life is the Denary System — base 10. In this system each digit used is said to have a PLACE VALUE which is a power of 10.

74

BESIDES THE DENARY SYSTEM, WHAT ARE THE OTHER SYSTEMS OF NOTATION ?

Binary System (Base 2), Ternary (Base 3), Quarternary (Base 4), Quinary (Base 5), Senary (Base 6), Septenary (Base 7), Octonary (Base 8), Nonary (Base 9), Undenary (Base 11) and Deudonary (Base 12).

75
WHAT IS 'DISTRIBUTIVE LAW' ?

It means that addition and subtraction may be performed in any order.

76
HOW DOES IT RELATE TO THE DISTRIBUTIVE LAW OF MULTIPLICATIONS ?

There is no relationship really. This means altogether another thing. Distributive Law of Multiplications means that the multiplication of a compound expression by a factor is the sum of the partial product of each terms of the expression by the factor. For example: $(a+b+c)d = ad+bd+cd$

77
WHAT DOES 'e' STAND FOR IN ARITHMETIC ?

e is the base of the Napier or Hyperbolic system of logarithms. $e = 2.71821828459045$.

78
WHAT IS 'ELIMINATE' ?

In Arithmetic Eliminate means to get rid of one or more unknown quantities from two or more simultaneous equations.

79
WHAT IS 'PERMILLAGE' ?

Permillage is the fraction with a stated numerator and an understood denominator of 1000. Just as % is the recognised mark for 'percent' ‰ is the sign for 'Per mill' (Latin, MILLE, a thousand).

80
WHAT IS THE 'AUSTRIAN METHOD' OF SUBTRACTION ?

The 'Austrian Method' of subtraction is generally used by shopkeepers in Europe while giving change to a customer. In the 'Austrian Method' instead of SUBTRACTING the amount of the purchase from the amount of the coin or bill given in payment, they add from the amount of the purchase upto the next higher money unit, then to the next, and so on until they come to the amount of the coin or bill given in payment.

For example, if the amount of purchase is £ 3-23 and the bill given in payment is £10-00. They give the customer the following money units for his change:

5 pence and 2 pence to make the sum £ 3-30, then two 10 pence to make the sum £ 3-50, then a 50 pence to make the sum £ 4-00 and finally six one pound notes to bring the sum upto £ 10-00.

81
WHAT IS A 'GRAPH' ?

A graph is the pictorial representation of Statistics. For example, if we want to show the comparative rainfall in a certain district from month to month, we draw a graph depicting a row of vertical glass tubes, one for each month, each of them shaded, to a depth which represents the number or inches of rainfall for that month.

Many other statistics can be reduced to simple graphs.

82
ARE STATISTICS ALWAYS DEPICTED IN GRAPHIC IN VERTICAL FORMS OR ARE THERE OTHER WAYS OF REPRESENTING THEM ?

There are two other ways. Graphs may be expressed in curved lines and horizontal bars also. When statistics are reduced to a simple group of figures, the correct form of graph will present itself without any trouble.

83
WHAT IS 'EVALUATE' ?

Evaluate means to work out a sum to its simplest form. In other words, to get the exact vlaue of a sum.

84
WHAT IS MEANT BY 'Casting out nines' ?

'Casting out the nines' is a method of checking
answers to multiplication, addition and subtraction.
It is based on the idea of finding the sum of the
digits in a number and then adding the digits in the
resulting sum, etc., until a one digit number results.
This addition of the digits in a number is further
simplified by first discarding or casting away any
digits whose sum is 9. The remainder is set down,
in each case as the check number. For example,
if you want to verify the following multiplication:

$8216 \times 4215 = 34630440$, this is how you proceed.

$8+2+1+6 = 17$, casting out the nines leaves 8 as
   check number.

$4+2+1+5 = 12$, casting out the nines levels 3 as
   check number.

$3+4+6+3+0+4+4+0 = 24$, casting the nines
   leaves 6 as check number.

$3 \times 8 = 24, 2+4 = 6$ which was the check number of
   the original product. So the multiplication is
   correct.

85
WHAT ARE 'FIGURATE NUMBERS' ?

They are just numbers or a series of numbers formed

from an arithmetical progression of which the first term is unity and the difference a whole number, by taking the first two, first three, first four, etc., terms and forming a new series or progressions, and so on, by being formed in the same way. The numbers of each sequence, when represented by points, can be systematically arranged in various geometrical figures such as triangles, pentagons, tetrahedrons, etc. Synonym of Polygonal Numbers.

86
WHAT ARE 'CRYPTOGRAMS' ?

Cryptograms are mathematical puzzles which are concerned with the association of the letters of the alphabet with the digits. In simple cryptogram each letter is replaced by one of the digits 0, 1, 2, 3, 4, 5, 6, 7, 8, 9 and n digit is represented by more than one letter. Of course, the cryptogram should make mathematical sense.

87
WHAT LED TO 'TEN' AS THE BASE OF THE GENERALLY USED NUMBER SYSTEM ?

The use of the fingers on both hands in counting led to the use of 'ten' as the base of the number system. Latter on symbols were used to represent numbers. In a certain tribe the word meaning 'three' was the word used for 'middle finger'.

88

WHAT IS THE ACTUAL USE OF ZERO IN THE NUMBER SYSTEM ?

Zero is used as a place holder when there is no frequency to record in a place in a number. For example, in the 809 0 holds ten's place, showing that there were no tens to record in the number. Zero is the symbol which makes it possible to show values in our number system without the use of an artificial means to identify place value.

89

HOW DID THE WORD 'DIGIT' ORIGINATE IN REFERENCE TO NUMBERS ?

The word 'digit' is derived from the Latin word 'digitus' which means 'finger'.

90

WHAT IS AN 'ABACUS' ?

The Abacus is a counting frame to aid in Arithmetic Computation—largely used in China and Japan. A simple form of Abacus consists of a series of parallel wires or rods fastened in a wooden frame. There are counters or beads which are moved along each rod. The position of each rod represents a certain place value.

91

WHAT EXACTLY IS THE FUNCTION OF A DECIMAL POINT ?

A number system is not complete unless it may be used to express fractional parts of a unit by means of place values. The decimal point identifies the one's place and therefore it serves as a separatrix between a unit and a part of a unit.

92

WHAT ARE 'MAGIC SQUARES' ?

Magic Squares consist of a number of integers arranged in the form of a square in such a way that the sum of the numbers in every row, in every column and each diagonal is the same. Magic Squares originated as an amusement in old times when mystical ideas were associated with particular numbers. Even before the Christian Era Magic Squares were constructed in China. Then introduction into Europe appears to have been in the early part of the fifteenth century.

A Magic Square engraved on a silver plate was sometimes prescribed as a charm against the plague.

93
WHAT IS A 'DIABOLIC MAGIC SQUARE' ?

The Diabolic Magic Square also, known as the Pan-diagonal Magic Square, is the one that satisfies the condition that the square should be magic along the broken diagonals as well as along the two ordinary diagonals. In other words, if a Diabolic Magic Square is cut into two pieces along a line between any two rows or any two columns, and the two

15	10	3	6
4	5	16	9
14	11	2	7
1	8	13	12

pieces are interchanged, the real square so formed will also be pandiagonally magic.

In the magic square given here, the sum of the numbers in each row, column and in the two diagonals is 34. And the sum of the numbers in the six broken diagonals formed by the numbers 15, 9, 2, 8, the numbers 10, 4, 7, 13, the numbers 3, 5, 14, 12 the numbers 6, 4, 11, 13, the numbers 3, 9, 14, 8, and the numbers 10, 16, 7, 1 all add upto 34.

A similar Diabolic Magic Square was inscribed at Khajuraho, India, around the twelfth century.

94
WHAT DOES 'GEOMETRICAL MEAN' MEAN IN ARITHMETIC ?

The Geometrical Mean of any number or numbers is the root of their product which is represented by their number. For example, the Geometrical Mean of two numbers is the square root of the product of the two numbers. The Geometrical Mean of three numbers is the cube root of the product of the three numbers.

95
WHAT IS THE ORIGIN OF MEASURE ?

The measure had its origin in something concrete

unlike numbers, which are abstract. To start with some parts of the human body was used as a basis for establishing a suitable standard for a measure of distance, and as each particular standard for a measure was established an effort was made to divide the standard into smaller units of measure. As such since there is no direct relationship between our system of number and our collection of measures, and as man learned to use different measures, he tried to make an arbitrary relationship between different units. Thus, the ratio of the foot to the yard became 1 to 3, and the ratio of the foot to the mile 1 to 5280.

96

WHY DOES A MILE HAVE TO BE 5280 FT ?

That's rather a funny number.

Roman soldiers counted 1000 double steps as a mile, from the Latin MILLE meaning THOUSAND, and a double step is between 5 and 6 ft. King Henry VII of England, in the fifteenth century changed it to exactly 8 furlongs, 8 × 220 yards which are equal to 5280 ft.

97

HOW DO THE 'UNITY FRACTIONS' RELATE TO FRACTIONS ?

If the numerator of a simple fraction is unity, it is

called a unity fraction. A complex fraction can be changed to a unity fraction by inverting the denominator or/and multiplying, or by multiplying numerator and denominator by the least common multiple of all denominators in the complex fraction. For example:

$$(\tfrac{1}{3}/ (\tfrac{1}{2} + \tfrac{1}{4}) = (12 \times \tfrac{1}{3})) (12 (\tfrac{1}{2} + \tfrac{1}{4})) = \tfrac{4}{9}$$

98

THERE ARE GENERALLY TWO UNITY FRACTIONS IN EVERY EQUATION. THEN HOW DO WE KNOW WHICH ONE TO USE ?

Use the one that makes it possible for you to cancel the units you do not need.

The equation 1 yard = 3 ft.

It gives two fractions $\dfrac{1 \text{ Yd}}{3 \text{ ft}}$ and $\dfrac{3 \text{ ft}}{1 \text{ Yd}}$

Both are, of course, equal to 1. In this case try one of the two fractions. If it works good. If not, try the other one.

99

HOW DOES THE METRIC SYSTEM COMPARE WITH THE ENGLISH SYSTEM ?

The metric is related to our system of numbers,

whereas the English system of Linear measures, in reality is not a system but a collection of independent measures. The units in the metric system are interrelated, and so they constitute a system. The comparison of the English System to Metric System is as follows :

English System

12 inches—1 foot
3 feet   —1 yard
5½ yards —1 rod
320 rods—1 mile

Metric System

10 millimetres —1 centimetre
10 centimetres —1 decimetre
10 decimetres —1 metre
10 metres   —1 decametre
10 decametres —1 hectametre
10 hectametres —1 kilometre

The metric system has been in use less than 150 years, whereas the English System of measures is as old as our number system.

100
HOW DID THE METRIC SYSTEM ORIGINATE ?

A Committee of Scientists in France, in the early part of the nineteenth century, formulated a system of measures, which is a decimal system—the same base as our number system. Since the metre is the Standard Unit in this system of linear measure, it came to be known as the METRIC System. In this system the measure is disassociated from any tangible object, such as the length of an arm or a foot.

A Meter, the Standard Unit of the Metric System is one-ten millionth of the distance from the equator to the pole along the meridian.

101
WHAT ARE THE ADVANTAGES OF THE METRIC SYSTEM OVER THE ENGLISH SYSTEM ?

Since Metric System was constructed as a decimal system by scientists who knew that number in general, and that it can be applied anywhere to any situation in which quantitative relationships are present, it is a much more practical system. On the other hand, the English System is a product of necessity, with its standards originating from tangible concrete things which had no relationship to our number system. The originators of these measures, perhaps, were unaware of the generality of a decimal system. Therefore, in this system we have unrelated units.

102
WHAT IS THE ORIGIN OF THE BASIC UNIT OF TIME ?

The basic practical unit of time is the mean Solar day. We define all other time units in terms of it.

A mean solar day is based on the average time needed for the earth to turn once on its axis.

103
WHAT IS A 'COMPLEX FRACTION' ?

A complex fraction has a fraction or mixed number for one or both of its terms, thus:

$$4\frac{3}{8} \qquad \frac{9}{3} \qquad 5\frac{1}{2}$$
$$(\frac{\quad}{\frac{5}{6}}); \text{ or} \qquad (7\overline{4}); \text{ or} \qquad (\frac{\quad}{9\frac{3}{4}})$$

104
WHAT IS 'IMPROPER' ABOUT AN IMPROPER FRACTION ?

A fraction is called an improper fraction, when its numerator is greater than its denominator. For example, $\frac{7}{3}$ or $\frac{9}{8}$. On the other hand a fraction is called a 'proper' fraction when it has a numerator, smaller than its denominator.

105
WHAT ARE 'HARMONIC MEANS' ?

When the Harmonic Progression is inverted and thereby turned into an Arithmetical progression, then after finding the required number of means by the method for Arithmetic Means, and these are inverted, they become the Harmonic Means required.

106
WHAT ARE 'EMPIRICAL PROBLEMS' ?

There are problems that are not necessarily supported by any established theory of laws but are based upon immediate experience rather than logical conclusions. Such problems are known as Empirical Problems. To give an example, if you come across a problem which says 'with the ten digits, 9, 8, 7, 6, 5, 4, 3, 2, 1, 0, express numbers whose sum is unity: each digit being used only once, and the use of the usual notations for fractions being allowed with the same ten digits express numbers whose sum is 100'.

There is no limit to the making of such questions, but their solutions involve little or no mathematical skill. These are considered Empirical Problems.

107
WHAT ARE 'ARITHMETICAL FALLACIES' ?

Sometimes certain problems are put leading to arithmetical results which are obviously impossible. Such problems are known as Arithmetical fallacies.

Here is an example:

Q. Prove $1 = 2$

Proof

Suppose that $a = b$

Then $ab = a^2$

$\therefore ab - b^2 = a^2 - b^2$

$\therefore b(a - b) = (a + b)(a - b)$

$\therefore b = a + b$

$\therefore b = 2b \therefore 1 = 2$

108
WHAT ARE 'ARITHMETICAL RESTORATIONS' ?

The class of problems dealing with the reconstruction of arithmetical sums from which various digits have been erased are called Arithmetical Restorations. This kind of exercise has attracted a good deal of attention in recent years.

109
WHAT IS 'GOLDBACH'S THEOREM' ?

That every number greater than 4 can be expressed as the sum of two odd primes. For example :

$$5 = 3 + 2, 7 = 5 + 2, 9 = 7 + 2$$

110
WHAT IS 'TOWER OF HANOI' IN ARITHMETIC ?

'Tower of Hanoi' is an Arithmetical puzzle brought out by M. Claus in 1883. The problem goes like this:

'There are three pegs fastened to a stand, consisting of eight circular discs of wood, each of which has a hole in the middle through which a peg can be passed. These discs are of different radii, and initially they are placed all on one peg, so that the biggest is at the bottom, and the radii of the successive discs decrease as we ascend: thus the smallest disc is at the top. This arrangement is called the TOWER. The problem is to shift the discs from one peg to another in such a way that a disc shall never rest on one smaller than itself, and finally to transfer the tower i.e. all the discs in their proper order from the peg on which they initially rested to one of the other pegs'.

The number of separate transfers of single discs which one must make to effect the transfer of the tower is:

18446744073709551615

111
WHAT ARE 'PRIME PAIRS' ?

A de Polignac has conjenctured that every even

number is the difference of two consecutive primes in infinitely many ways. Suppose we take the even number to be 2, this means that there are infinitely many pairs of primes that are consecutive odd numbers such as 5, 7; 11, 13; 17, 19; 29, 31; 41, 43; 59, 61; 71, 73; these are called prime pairs.

112
WHAT IS 'KARAT' ?

In the Troy weight, which is used by jewellers in weighing precious metals and stones, a Carat is equal to 3.168 grains. The term Karat is a variation of Carat and in form is used in comparing the parts of gold alloys which are in gold.

The comparison is based on the use of 24 Karats to mean pure gold, and therefore 14 Karats means $\frac{14}{24}$ pure gold by weight or 14 parts pure gold and 10 parts alloy.

113
WHAT IS A 'CONDITIONAL EQUATION' ?

An equation is a symbolic statement that two quantities are equal in value. When an equation is true for all values of the letters, it is an *identity*, for example: $4a + 9a = 13a$. However, when this is not the case, it is known as a Conditional Equation. For example:

x + 5 = 3x — 3. In this case the formula is true only if x = 4. Only then 4 + 5 = 12 — 3 or 9 = 9

114
WHAT IS A 'FACTRORIAL' ?

Factorial is the product of all positive integers from 1 up to a given number n, inclusive. Factorial is denoted by the symbol n !

115
HOW DOES FACTORIAL RELATE TO FACTORING?

There is no connection at all. Factoring is another thing altogether. Factoring is actually the process of finding two or more expressions whose product is a given expression.

116
WHAT ARE 'GILLS' ?

Gills is a term used in Liquid Measure. Sixteen fluid ounces or 1 pint is equal to 4 Gills.

117

HOW DO YOU EXPLAIN pi (π) IN A SIMPLE WAY?

Many practical problems are concerned with the measurements of a circle. And the basic to the measurements is the fact that the *ratio of the circumference to its diameter is a constant.* No matter what the size of the circle the ratio remains the same. In mathematics, this ratio is represented by the Greek letter π (pi).

However this constant is not an integer and much effort has been spent to find the value of this ratio. It has been evaluated to a large number of decimal points by electronic calculators.

The story of the accuracy to which the value of pi is known is an interesting one.

In the Bible, the value of pi is used as 3 Archimedes had declared the value of pi as less than $3\frac{1}{7}$ but greater than $3\frac{10}{71}$. The value generally used today 3.1416 was known at the time of Ptolemy (A.D. 150).

In 1949, with the use of the Computer Eniac, a group of mathematicians calculated 2037 decimals of pi in 70 hours.

And recently Daniel Shanks and John Wrench have published pi to 100,000 decimals. It took them 8 hours and 43 minutes on an IBM 7090 system to compute this result.

However for practical use the approximation of pi 3.1416 is sufficient.

118
WHAT IS THE 'LUDOLPHIAN NUMBER' ?

At the end of Sixteenth Century Ludolph Van Ceulen calculated 35 decimal place for pi. In his will, he requested that these 35 numbers be engraved on his tombstone. This was done. In Germany they still refer to this number as 'Ludolphian Number'.

119
WHAT ARE 'SIGNIFICANT DIGITS' ?

'Significant Digits' is used in context to decimal numbers. The significant digits of a decimal number are those beginning with the first one, reading from left to right, which is not zero and ending with the last are definitely specified.
For example:

.444 has three significant digits
2.8943 has five significant digits
0.005182 has four significant digits.

120
WHAT IS 'ROUNDING OFF' IN ARITHMETIC ?

To 'Round off' a decimal number means to correct it to a specified number off significant digits. The following rule is followed:

a. The number of non-zero digits are retained and the rest on the right of this are discarded.

b. If the digit to the immediate right of the last digit retained is greater than 5, the last digit retained is increased by 1.

c. If the digit to the immediate right of the last digit retained is less than five, the last digit is left unchanged.

121
WHAT IS AN 'INCOMMENSURABLE' NUMBER ?

This is actually a ratio, which is not expressed exactly by two whole numbers.

For example:

$\frac{1}{3}: \frac{7}{6}$ or 2.56:5.74 or 2:5

having no common measure.

122

WHAT IS A 'TRANSFINITE CARDINAL NUMBER' ?

A Cardinal number of an infinite set is called a Transfinite Cardinal Number.

123

WHAT IS MEANT BY 'RELATIVELY PRIME' NUMBER ?

When we reduce a fraction, for example:

$$\frac{60}{4880} = \frac{(2^2 \times 5) \times 3}{(2^2-5) \times (2^2 \times 61)} = \frac{3}{2^2 \times 61} = \frac{3}{244}$$

Since 3 is the only prime factor of the numerator and 3 is not a factor of the denominator, the fraction $\frac{60}{4880}$ is in its lowest terms. Since the numerator and the denominator do not have any common prime factors they are said to be 'relatively prime'.

124

WHAT IS 'FOUR-COLOUR' PROBLEM ?

About the middle of the 19th century, this problem known as the 'Four colour' problem related to map making was proposed and remains insolved to this date. The problem involves the colouring of maps using at most four colours. When two countries have common boundaries, they must have different colours. When two countries have only **single** points in common they may use the same colour.

No one, so far, has been able to produce a map that would require more than four colours. But no one has been able to prove that four colours are sufficient for all maps.

However, it has been proved that if a map could be drawn that would require five colours, there would have been at least 36 countries on it. And it has also been proved that five colours are sufficient for all maps, but may not be necessary.

125
WHAT IS A 'GOOGOL' ?

Googol is one of the largest numbers that has ever been named. It has been defined as 1 followed by one hundred zeros;

10000000000000000000000000000000000000000000 00000000000000000000000000000000000000000000 0000000000000

However, a googol can be expressed using exponents, as

$$10^{100}$$

126
WHAT IS A 'GOOGOLPLEX'

Even larger than the googol is googolplex. It is defined as 1 followed by a googol of zeros. It is claimed that there would not even be room between the earth and the moon to write all the zeros in a googolplex!

127
HOW WOULD YOU NAME A SIXTYONE DIGITS NUMBER SUCH AS THIS: 7, 346, 648, 004, 560, 986, 215, 348, 444, 286, 445, 305, 146, 039, 140, 046, 960, 678, 582, 256, 003 ?

SEVEN VIGINTILLION, THREE HUNDRED FORTY SIX NOVEMDECILLION, SIX HUNDRED FORTY EIGHT OCTODECILLION, FOUR SEPTENDECLLION, FIVE HUNDRED SIXTY SEXDECILLION, NINE HUNDRED EIGHTYSIX QUINDECILLION, TWO HUNDRED FIFTEEN QUATTOUR DECILLION, THREE HUNDRED FORTY EIGHT DUODECILLION, FOUR HUNDRED FORTY FOUR UNDECILLION, TWO HUNDRED EIGHTY-SIX DECILLION, FOUR HUNDRED FORTY FIVE MONILLION, THREE HUNDRED AND FIVE OCTILLION, ONE HUNDRED FORTY SIX SEPTILLION, THIRTY NINE SEXTIL-LION, ONE HUNDRED FORTY QUINTIL-

LION, FORTY SIX QUADRILLION, NINE
HUNDRED SIXTY TRILLION, SIX HUND-
RED SEVENTY EIGHT BILLION, FIVE
HUNDRED EIGHTY TWO MILLION, TWO
HUNDRED FIFTY SIX THOUSAND AND
THREE.

128
WHAT IS AN 'INDEPENDENT VARIABLE' ?

A quantity which may have any value we care to
give it is an Independent Variable. The value of
the corresponding variable is given is fixed as soon
as the value of the independent variable is known.
For example in the equation $x + 5 = y$ we give x
the value 9, then automatically the dependent
variable y becomes 14.

129
WHAT IS A 'TRANSCENDENTAL NUMBER' ?

A number which is not algebraic is called transcendental. In other words a transcendental number
satisfies no algebraic equation whose coefficients
are rational numbers.

130

A CERTAIN NUMBER IS ATTACHED TO THE MAIDEN GODDESS ATHENE. WHAT ARE SOME OF THE OTHER NUMBERS ATTACHED TO ?

Number SEVEN is attached to the maiden Goddess Athene 'because seven alone within the decade has neither factors nor product'. Five suggested marriage, the union of the first even and first genuine odd number. One was identified with reason. Two with opinion—a wavering fellow is Two, he does not know his own mind. And FOUR with justice, steadfast and square.

131

HOW DID THE WORD 'CALCULATE' ORIGINATE ?

When people first began to count, little by little they found out how to add, subtract, multiply and divide. And in some countries special devices were invented to make computation easier, especially in dealing with large numbers. The Romans used a counting frame, which is today known as Abacus, in which units, fives, ten and so on were represented by heads, which could be moved in grooves.

These heads were called CALCULI which is plural for CALCULUS or pebble. Since CALC means lime and marble is a kind of lime-stone, it is clear the heads were of marble.

This is the origin of the word CALCULATE.

132
WHAT IS CUNEIFORM WRITING OF NUMERALS ?

It is a kind of a wedge shaped writing of numerals, which developed in the Mesapotamia valley, and was very much in use in ancient times. Lack of other writing materials led the people to stamp inscriptions on clay bricks with sticks which usually were triangular with sharp edges.

The Cuneiform numerals for 1, 2 and 3 are ∇ $\nabla\nabla$ $\nabla\nabla\nabla$.

133
WHAT IS THE DIFFERENCE BETWEEN AN INTEGER AND AN INTEGRAL ?

The integer is a whole number as opposed to a fraction such as 3, 6, 8, 15, 1284. Whereas integral means consisting of a whole number or an undivided quantity.

134
WHAT IS 'INTERPOLATION' ?

It is a verb meaning, filling in the intermediate terms of a series of numbers or to insert the intermediate terms of a series.

135
WHAT IS AN 'EQUIVALENT FRACTION' ?

Such fraction that have the same value, but are written differently are equivalent. For example :

$$1\tfrac{1}{4} = \tfrac{5}{4} = \tfrac{10}{8} = \tfrac{20}{16}$$

136
IS THERE ANY DIFFERENCE BETWEEN PERCENT AND PERCENTAGE ?

Yes there is a good deal of difference, though they sound alike. Percent shown with the symbol % is a rate like 10%, whereas 'percentage' is a number expressed as a percent of some other number.

137
HOW DID THE WORD 'TON' ORIGINATE ? WHY SHOULD THERE BE 2,000 POUNDS IN A TON, AND WHY NOT 1000 ?

The word ton originates from the word tub. And a wine maker's tub which is also known as tun traditionally fills 250. One gallon bottles of wine each weighing about 8 pounds.

138
WHAT IS A 'LITERAL EQUATION' ?

A Literal Equation is an equation in which letters are used to represent numbers. In mathematics that arise in business and work it is often necessary to find the value of a Literal Expression when the numerical values of the letter variables are given. This process is known as 'evaluating' the equation.

139
WHAT IS MEANT BY 'ANTILOG' ?

'Antilog' is generally written in front of a number and it means 'Look up in the table the value of the base when raised to the power represented by the number'.

140
WHAT IS 'SAND RECKONER' ?

Archimedes wrote, a short treatise in which he made an estimate of the number of grains of Sand in the world. This treatise is known as 'Sand Reckoner'. In this work he hit upon two of the most powerful peculiarities which is a part of the modern number script. He declared that all high numbers should be represented by multiples of simple powers of ten, and he also hit upon the law which underlies the modern calculating device called *logarithms*.

141
WHAT IS 'CLYPSYDRAS' ?

The Alexandrians and the Chinese invented 'Clypsydras' to replace the sundial, which were kept going by a flow of water.

142
'WHAT IS 'MANTISSA' ?

The positive fractional part of the logarithm is called MANTISSA. For example to find the logarithm of 9.876 in the table, we look down the lefthand side of the table, through the column of double figures beginning with 10, until we find 98. At the top of the page there are columns headed by the numbers 0 to 9. We look along the line beginning 98 till we come to the column headed 7. The number given in this place is 9,943. This is the Mantissa of the logarithm of 9.87.

143
WHAT IS 'RHYND PAPYRUS' ?

In the ancient times the Egyptian writer Ahmes

wrote down the laws of measuring things. This is
known as Rhynd papyrus. However the plain man
could not decipher this writing.

144
WHAT IS 'INVOLUTION' ?

The method used for obtaining any power for any
quantity is known as 'Involution'. The power of a
number is obtained by multiplying the logarithm
of the number by the index representing the power
required. The product thus acquired is the logarithm of the number required.

145
WHAT IS 'MYRIAD' ?

An immense number, innumerable number, is
called Myriad. It can also mean ten thousand.

146
WHAT ARE 'QUARTER SQUARES' ?

The product of two numbers is equal to the
difference of one-fourth the squares of their sum
and their difference:

$\frac{1}{4}(a + b)^2 - \frac{1}{4}(a - b)^2$. This fact has been used to reduce multiplication to addition with the aid of tables of quarter squares. The method is very old. There are many tables of quarter squares and the most extensive table lists quarter squares of integers upto 200,000. The method is very useful and economical.

147
WHAT ARE 'QUARTERNIONS' ?

If you do not use the properties of order and the commutative law of multiplication, we obtain an interesting further extension of the complex number system known as Quarternions q.v. in abbreviation.

Quarternions are of the form $a + bi + cj + dk$ where a, b, c, d are real.

148
WHAT IS THE 'THEORY OF NUMBERS' ?

The Theory of Numbers is concerned with the study of the properties of integers or whole numbers. The proofs of many of the Theory use the deepest resources of mathematics. However, some of the most interesting conjectures are still unproved.

Topics of the Theory of the Numbers can be listed as follows?

I. Divisibility and Primality:

    a. Elementary Definitions; Factorizations into Primes.

    b. Residue Classes; Eulers Theorem

    c. Congruences in one unknown

    d. Quadratic Residues; The Quadratic Reciprocity Law

    e. Factorization of Numbers; Mersenne Primes

II. Representation by forms:

    a. Binary Quadratic forms

    b. Genera of Quadratic forms; Formulas for Number of Representations

    c. The Numbers Represented by a Quadratic Form: universal forms Representation of zero.

    d. Automorphs and Reduction of indefinite Binary Quadratic Forms

    e. Diophantine Equations

III. Topics in Analytic Number Theory:

    a. Gauss's Class-Number Conjencture

    b. Distribution of Primes; Asymptotic Formulas

IV. Additive Theory of Numbers:

    a. Partitions

    b. The waring problem and related problems

c. The Goldbach problem

V. Diophontine Approximation:

a. Geometry of Numbers

b. Diophontine Approximation

VI. Generalisations of Arithmetic:

a. Algebraic Numbers

b. Ideals

c. Algebras and their Arithmetics

149
WHAT IS 'DYADIC NOTATION' ?

Dyadic Notation is another name for Binary Notation.

150
WHAT IS 'FERMAT'S LAST THEOREM' ?

In the margin of his copy of 'Diophantus' Fermat wrote: 'If n is a number greater than two, there are no whole numbers a, b, c such that $a^n + b^n = c^n$. I have found a truly wonderful proof which this margin is too small to contain'. Unfortunately, he died soon after, and this theory has never been proved, though almost every great mathematician for the last three centuries has attempted a proof.

Some skeptics, however, believe Fermat himself never solved.

151
WHAT ARE 'DIGITAL COMPUTERS' ?

A digital computer consists of three parts:

1. Store
2. Executive Unit
3. Control

The store is a store of information and memory. The executive unit is a part which carries out the various individual operations involved in a calculation. And it is the duty of the Control that the instructions fed to the machine are obeyed correctly and in the proper order.

152
WHAT IS MEANT BY 'ASSOCIATIVE LAW' ?

Associative Law means that the terms of an expression means connected by plus or minus signs can be grouped in any manner.

For example:

$a + b - c + d - c + f = (a + b) - c + (d - e) + f = a + (b - c) + d - (e - f)$

153

WHAT IS THE 'ASSOCIATIVE LAW OF MULTIPLICATION' ?

Here the meaning is that the factors of a product can be grouped in anyway we please.

For example:

$$(3a \times 4bc) \times d = b \times d \times 3 \times a \times 4 \times c$$
$$= (bd)(3ac)4$$

154

WHAT DOES 'COMMUTATIVE LAW' MEAN ?

The terms or parts of an expression which are connected by plus or minus signs can be written in any order is the Commutative Law. For example:

$$3 - 6 + 10 = -6 + 3 + 10 = 10 + 3 - 6 = 7$$

155

WHAT IS THE 'COMMUTATIVE LAW OF MULTIPLICATION' ?

The factors of any product may be taken in any order—this is the Commutative Law of Multiplication.

For example: $3a \times 4bc \times d = 3 \times a \times 4 \times b \times c \times d = 12abcd$

156
WHAT IS 'DISTRIBUTIVE LAW' ?

That addition and subtraction can be performed in any order.

157
WHAT IS 'DISTRIBUTIVE LAW OF MULTIPLICA-TION' ?

That the product of a Compound expression and a factor is the algebraical sum of the partial products of each term of the compound expression and the factor. For example:

$$(a + b + c) \, d = ad + bd + cd$$

158
WHAT IS MEANT BY THE 'INDEX LAW OF DIVISION' ?

That if in the numerator and the denominator of a fraction the same letter occurs, then the answer is the difference of the indices of the letters. For example:

$$\frac{a^5}{a^2} = a^3 \text{ or } \frac{b^4}{b^7} = \frac{1}{b^3} \text{ or}$$

$$\frac{a^3b^4}{a^5b^2} = \frac{b^2}{a^2}$$

159
WHAT IS 'INDEX LAW OF MULTIPLICATION' ?

That the final index of a letter occuring more than once in a product is the sum of the indices of that letter.

For example :

$$a^2 \times a^5 \times a^7 = a^{2+5+7} = a^{14} \text{ or } a^2b^2 \times a^7b^3$$

160
CAN YOU ADD, DIVIDE OR MULTIPLY PER CENT NUMBERS ?

No. It cannot be done. Normal arithmetical operations cannot be carried out with per cent numbers. Per cent helps you compare two numbers. For example when you say 'Sixty per cent of the people who attended the function were women'. What you are actually doing is you are comparing with the total number of people who attended the function.

161
WHAT IS THE DIFFERENCE BETWEEN MEASUREMENT NUMBERS AND ORDINARY NUMBERS ?

Measurement numbers are very much like the ordinary numbers in arithmetic. They can be added, subtracted, multiplied and divided. However while doing these operations one has to convert all measurement numbers into the same units. For example we cannot add 4 ft. and 9 inches to 6 of anything. We have to convert so that both measurements are either in foot units or inch units.

162
WHY IS THERE NO METRIC TIME UNIT ? IN OTHER WORDS, WHY CAN'T WE USE MULTIPLES OF TEN INSTEAD OF 60 SECONDS, 60 MINUTES, 24 HOURS, 7 DAYS IN A WEEK AND 365 DAYS IN A YEAR ?

It was suggested once. And indeed it would be a more practical system. But every country in the world uses the present system and no one wants a change.

163
WHAT IS THE 'CONCEPT OF TEMPERATURE' ?

When we set the oven at 375° degrees temperature to bake a cake or learn from a doctor that we have a fever of 103° or it is 70°F in Bangalore we are using the concept of temperature. To read the body temperature we have standard thermometers which are marked with numerical temperature scales agreed upon around the world. There are two temperature scales Fahrenheit and Centigrade.

164

HOW DID THE FAHRENHEIT AND CENTIGRADE TEMPERATURE SCALES ORIGINATE ?

The first modern temperature scale is Fahrenheit scale. This was devised in 1714 by a scientist named Gabriel Robert Fahrenheit. Fahrenhiet temperature scales is in common use for weather reports, medical thermometers and cook books. However this scale was improved by Anders Celsius, a Swedish Astronomer and his new temperature scale has been adopted in many countries of the world. However, most English speaking countries have continued to use the Fahrenheit scale and refer to the Celsius scale as Centigrade meaning 100 units temperature scale.

The Centigrade temperature unit has been set up using two reference temperatures: the temperature at which water normally freezes to ice was set as 0°C and the temperature at which water normally boils was set 100°C.

100 units on the Centigrade scale corresponds to 180 units on the Fahrenheit scale.

165

IS THERE ANY QUICK ARITHMETICAL METHOD OF CONVERTING FAHRENHEIT TO CENTIGRADE OR FROM CENTIGRADE TO FAHRENHEIT ?

Yes, there is a way. The two temperature scales are connected by a simple algebraic equation :

$$\frac{C + 40}{F + 40} = \frac{5}{9} \text{ Where C}$$

stands for the Centigrade temperature and F is the equivalent of Fahrenheit temperature. In order to convert Fahrenheit temperature degrees into Centigrade degrees all one has to do is rearrange the above equation as

$$C = \frac{5 (F—32)}{9}$$

166

WHAT IS THE MEASUREMENT USED IN SELLING LUMBER ?

Lumber is sold according to a special measure of volume called the board foot. The number of board feet= Thickness in inches

width in feet × length in feet

In case we want to calculate in board feet a Lumber that is 8 foot long 2 by 4 this is how we go about it :

Number of board feet $= 2 \text{ in} \times \frac{4}{12}\text{ft} \times$

$8 \text{ ft} = \frac{64}{12}\text{ft.} = 5.3 \text{ board foot.}$

2 inches is the thickness in inches

$\dfrac{4}{12}$ ft is the width in feet

8 ft. is the length in feet.

167
WHAT IS A 'LITERAL COEFFICIENT' ?

A letter which has fixed value is a Literal Coefficient. Usually the letters at the beginning of the alphabet are used for this purpose. For example to save time, when you want to write down 56398246 each time in a sum or if its value although fixed is unknown then this number may be called a, b, c, or any other letter of the alphabet.

168
WHAT IS 'MENSURATION' ?

Mensuration is the skill of measuring the length of lines, areas of surfaces, and volumes of solids from simple data of lines and angles.

169
WHAT IS THE DIFFERENCE BETWEEN MONOMIAL EXPRESSION AND MULTINOMIAL EXPRESSION ?

Monomial is an expression just one term such as 3, 4, 6x etc. Whereas Multinomial is an expression of more than three terms such as $3a+6b+9cd+4abc$

170
WHAT IS A 'NUMERICAL COEFFICIENT' ?

Numerical coefficient is an arithmetical number used in an expression such as 3, 8, 26.

171
WHY IS NUMBER 13 CALLED UNLUCKY ?

No one knows the exact reason, though some one gave me a flimsy one that it being the fifth prime number it was unlucky. However quite frankly I think it is really strange and unjustified. Many buildings in Europe and USA have no 13th floors, hotels have no rooms numbered 13, many people refuse to take car numbers that contains number 13, and people often refuse to start a journey or a new business on the 13th day of the month. In my own case, however, 13 has been a very lucky number.

In ancient Greece the 13 day of the month was considered unlucky for sowing but lucky for reaping.

172

THE NUMBER 9^{9^9} IS CONSIDERED A VERY INTE-RESTING NUMBER. WHY ?

Ninth power of the ninth power of nine is the largest in the world of numbers that can be expressed with just 3 digits. No one has been able to compute this yet. The very task is staggering to the mind

The answer to this number will contain 369 million digits. And to read it normally it would take more than a year. To write down the answer, you would require 1164 miles of paper.

173

WHAT IS THE BIGGEST KNOWN PRIME NUMBER ?

Tables containing the 664580 primes upto 10,000000 have been prepared. The largest known prime is :

$$2^{127}-1 = 17014118346046923173168$$
$$7303715884105727$$

174

HOW ARE THE SMALLEST MEASUREMENTS EXPRESSED ?

There are two units used in the measure of all small

distances, the micron (μ) and the Angstron Unit (Å. u.). A micron is the millionth of a metre and there are about 25000 microns in an inch. One Angstron unit equals one ten thousand millionth of a metre. One micron equals 10,000 times the length of an Angstron Unit.

Breadth of a hair = 75b

Diameter of red blood corpuscle = 2μ

Diameter of spherical bacterium = 0.5μ

Diameter of molecule of water = 0.00205μ

or 2.5 A.μ.

175
IS 1729 UNLUCKY ?

1729 is the only known number that is a sum of two cubes in two different ways.

$13^3 + 9^3 = 3729; 12^3 + 1^3 = 1729$

This is popularly known as Ramanujan's number. The great Indian Mathematician, was sick in the hospital, Prof. Hardy, his tutor paid him a visit. Prof. Hardy told Ramanujan that he rode a taxi to the hospital with a very unlucky number, 1729.

Ramanujan's face lit up with a smile and he said that it was not an unlucky number at all, but a very interesting number, the only number that can be represented as the sum of two different cubes in two different ways.

176

IS IT TRUE THAT SOME PEOPLE BELIEVE THAT ODD NUMBERS ARE LUCKY ?

Yes, even from olden days some people believe that odd numbers are lucky. Here is a stanza from 'Lover, Rory O'More' written in 1839.

Then Rory, the rogue, stole his arm round her neck,
So soft and so white, without freckle or speck;
And he look'd in her eyes, that were beaming with light,
And he kissed her sweet lips—don't you think he was right?
"Now, Rory leave off, sir, you'll hug me no more,
That's eight times today that you've kissed me before."
"Then here goes another," says he, "to make sure,
For there's luck in odd numbers," says Rory O'More.

177

WHAT IS AN 'ABUNDANT NUMBER' ?

When a number itself is greater than the sum of its factors, it is said to be an abundant number. It can also be called excessive number or redundant number.

178
WHAT IS 'AMPERE' ?

Ampere is the unit measure of electric current. The *absolute ampere* which is the legal standard of current since 1950 is the current in each of two long parallel wires which carry equal currents and for which there is a force of 2.10^{-7} newton permeter acting on each wire. However before 1950, the legal standard of current was the international ampere which is the current when passed through a solution of silver nitrate deposits silver at the rate of 0.001 118 grammes per second. One international ampere equals 0.999835 absolute ampere. Other units of electric current are milliamp (mA)$=10^{-3}$ A and microamp (μA) $= 10A^{-6}$

179
WHEN YOU SAY 'NEWTON PERMETER', WHAT EXACTLY IS NEWTON PERMETER ?

Newton permeter is a unit force. A force of one newton is a force which will give an acceleration of one meter per second to a mass of one kilogram.

180
WHAT IS THE GAME CALLED 'NIM' ?

'Nim' a favourite game of mathematicians, is said to have originated in Japan.

In this game two players draw articles from several piles, each player in turn taking as many as he pleases from any one pile. The player who draws the last article is the loser.

If the numbers of article in each heap is expressed in the Binary scale, the game readily lends itself to mathematical analysis.

There is one other way of playing this game. Three or more numbers in decimal system are written down, and two players move alternatively. Each player may reduce one and only one of the integers by any amount he wishes except zero. The winner is the one who obtains all zeros.

181
WHAT IS 'ANNUITY' ?

Annuity is the sum of money payable in a series of payment at regular intervals, under an annuity contract setting forth the amount of the annuity, its cost and the conditions under which it is to be paid. This contract is also known as the Annuity Policy when the annuity is a temporary one.

182
WHAT IS A 'PICTOGRAM' ?

Pictogram is any figure showing numerical relations such as graphs.

183
WHAT IS 'POUNDAL' ?

Poundal is a unit of force. The force which, acting on a mass of one pound for one second, will increase the velocity of the mass one foot per second is called a force of one Poundal.

184
WHAT IS 'AHMES RHYND PAPYRUS' ?

It is said to be the oldest mathematical book written about 1550 B.C.

185
WHAT IS 'ALEPH' ?

It is the first letter of the Hebrew alphabet written as $_oN^o_o$. The cardinal number of all countably infinite sets is called ALEPH-NULL or ALEPH ZERO. It is written as $_oN^o_o$. The cardinal number of all real numbers is designated by C.

186
WHAT IS A 'COIN-MATCHING GAME' ?

This is a two person game, in which each of the players tosses a coin of like value and if the two coins show like faces, either both heads or both tails, the first player wins, but if they show unlike faces the second player wins.

187
WHAT IS AN 'ABRIDGED MULTIPLICATION' ?

This is a process of multiplying whereby you drop a digit of the multiplier after each multiplication. You only drop such digits which do not affect the degree of accuracy desired. If in a product you need only two decimal place accuracy, you only need to retain the third place throughout the multiplication.

188
WHAT IS 'ORACLE' ?

'ORACLE' is an automatic digital computing machine at the Oak Ridge National Laboratory in the USA. ORACLE is an acronym for Oak Ridge Automatic Computer and Logical Engine.

189

**WHAT IS THE CONNECTION BETWEEN PERMUTA-
TION AND COMBINATION ?**

Permutation is an ordered arrangement of all or
part of a set of things. For example all possible permutations of the letters a, b and c are: a, b, c, ab,
ac, ba, bc, ca, cb, abc, acb, bac, cab and cba.

Combination of a set of objects is any selection of
one or more of the objects without regard to order.
The number of combinations of 'n' things 'r' at a
time is the number of sets that can be made up
from the 'n' things, each set containing 'r' different
things and no two sets containing exactly the same
'r' things. This is equal to the number of permutations of the 'n' things taken 'r' at a time, divided by
the number of permutations of 'r' things taken 'n'
at a time

190

WHAT IS THE MEANING OF PROBABILITY ?

Here is a quotation about Probability by Bishop
Butler:

"That which chiefly constitutes Probability is expressed in the World Likely, i.e. like some Truth,
or true Event; like it, in itself, in its Evidence, in
some more or fewer of its Circumstances. For when
we determine a thing to be probably true , . . 'Its
from the Mind's remarking in it a Likeness to some

other Event, which we have observed has come to pass."

If an event can occur in 'a' ways and the chance of it not occurring is in 'b' ways the probability of it occurring is $\dfrac{a}{a+b}$ and of its failing is $\dfrac{b}{a+b}$

Therefore, in a group of 29 waiting outside a movie house to buy ticket for the movie only five tickets are available, then the probability of any one particular person getting a ticket is $\dfrac{5}{29}$

and of his not getting a ticket is $\dfrac{24}{29}$

For another example, if one handkerchief is to be drawn from a bag containing two white handkerchieves and three black handkerchieves the probability of drawing a white handkerchief is $\frac{2}{5}$ and the probability of drawing a black handkerchief is 3/5.

191
WHAT IS 'RADIX' ?

Radix is any number which is made the fundamental number or base of any system of numbers. For example, 10 is the Radix of the decimal system of numeration. It can also be described as the base of a system of Logarithms.

192
WHAT IS 'RECIPROCAL' ?

The Reciprocal literally means Complimentary, inverted or mutually interchangeable. However in arithmetic it is used to denote different kinds of mutual relations The reciprocal of a number is the number whose product with the given number is equal to 1. For a fraction, the reciprocal is the fraction formed by interchanging the numerator and denominator in the given fraction.

For example the reciprocal of 2 is 1/2 or 0.5

$\dfrac{a}{b}$ is the reciprocal of $\dfrac{b}{a}$

193
WHAT IS 'REGULA FALSI' ?

Literally translated it means 'rule of false position'. In Arithmetic it is the method of calculating an unknown by making an estimate and working from it and properties of the unknown to secure the value of the latter.

194
WHAT IS A 'SCALE' ?

The scale is a system of marks in a given order, at

known intervals. It is used in the aids used for measuring quantities like rulers and thermometers.

195
WHAT IS 'SEPARATRIX' ?

The mark that separates like the comma, full-stop, colon or a semicolon. The decimal point is also called a Separatrix sometimes.

196
SEXAGESIMAL, DOES IT HAVE ANYTHING TO DO WITH SEX ?

No. Sexagesimal means 'pertaining to the number sixty.' For example 'Sexagesimal system of Numbers'. This is a number system using sixty for a base instead of ten.

197
WHAT IS A 'SUB-FACTORIAL' ?

To find the Sub-Factorial of an integer, supposing 'n' is the integer the Sub-Factorial of $n = n! \times$

$(\frac{1}{2}! - \frac{1}{3}! + \frac{1}{4}! \ldots \quad \frac{(-1)n)}{n!})$

For example the Sub-factorial of $4 = 4!$ $(\frac{1}{2}! + \frac{1}{3}! + \frac{1}{4}!)$

$$= 24 \ \frac{(1}{(2} - \frac{1}{6} + \frac{1)}{24)} = 9$$

198
WHAT IS A 'SUB-SEQUENCE' ?

A sequence within a sequence.

For example $\frac{1}{2}$, $\frac{1}{4}$ . . .1 $/(2n$ is a subsequence of 1, $\frac{1}{2}$, $\frac{1}{3}$, $\frac{1}{4}$, . . . $1/n)$

199
WHAT IS A 'SUB-MULTIPLE' ?

It is a number or quantity which divides another exactly. For example:

8 is a sub-multiple of 72 and $a + x$ is a sub-multiple of $a^2 - x^2$.

200
WHAT IS 'SURD' ?

Surd is the root of a number which can only be found approximably. It can also be called a numerical expression containing an irrational number. It is sometimes used as a synonym of irrational number.

201
WHAT IS 'THEORY' ?

Theory is the principles concerned with a certain concept, and the facts postulated and proved about it.

202
WHAT IS A 'VANISHING FRACTION' ?

Vanishing fraction is a fraction which becomes zero in the end.

203
WHAT IS 'UNIQUE' IN ARITHMETIC'?

Consisting or leading to one and only one result. The product of two integers are unique, but the square root or a cube root of an integer is not.

204
WHAT IS 'UNITARY' ?

Relating to a unit or units. Undivided.

205
WHAT IS 'WARING'S PROBLEM' ?

This problem was solved by Hilbert in 1909. The problem, however, was first proposed by Waring, of showing that, for any integer n, there is an integer K (n) such that any integer can be represented as the sum of not more than K(n) numbers, each of which is an 'nth' power of an integer. Any integer can be represented as the sum of not more than 4 squares, and as the sum of not more than 9 cubes.

206
WHAT IS 'ZENO'S PARADOX OF ACHILLES AND THE TORTOISE' ?

This is what is known as the Zeno's famous puzzle. Zeno showed that the mathematical treatment of space and time required that they be broken up into infinite sets of points and instants.

A tortoise has a head start on Achilles equal distance from a to b and both start running. Achilles runs after the tortoise. Though Achilles runs faster than the tortoise, he would never catch up with the tortoise, since while Achilles goes from a to b, the tortoise goes from b to c, and Achilles goes from b to c the tortoise goes from c to d and so on. This process never ending. Well, there is only one explanation to the fallacy—that motion is measured by space intervals per unit of time and not by numbers of points.

207
WHAT ARE 'MNEMONICS' ?

Mnemonics are devices for memorizing bits of information by associating them with things that are easier to remember. The most common Mnemonic device for remembering a series of digits is a sentence or a rhyme in which the number of letters in each word corresponds to the digits in the desired order.

In the sentence 'May I have a large container of coffee?' the value of P (π) to seven places of decimals are contained. The number of letter in each word corresponds to the successive integers in the decimal expansion of π.

Sir James Jeans came out with the following sentence, in which the value of π is contained upto 14 decimal places : How I want a drink, Alcoholic of course, after the heavy chapters involving Quantum Mechanics' 3 14 15 92 65 35 89 79.

Adam C Orn of Chicago published in the *Literary Digest* of Chicago of the 20th January 1906 issue on page 83, the following poem that contains to 30 decimal places :

Now I—even I, would celebrate

In Rhymes unapt the great

Immortal Syracusan rivalled never more,

Who in his wonderous lore

Passed on before,

Left men his guidance

How to circles mensurate. 3 14 15 92 65 35 89 75
43 23 94 62 64 338 3279

208

WHY IS NUMBER 99 CALLED DOCTOR'S NUMBER ?

For a doctor the number 99 is very important,
because when he listens to the chest of a patient
through Stethoscope, he asks the patient to say
repeatedly ninety nine. The normal resonance this
vocalisation would cause is increased if the under-
lined lung has solidified or became pneumonic. In
other words vocalisation of ninety nine helps the
doctor to diagnose pneumonia at the bedside.

If you have ninetynine sounding louder than the
normal in a particular area you know that the lung
in that area has become solidified or pneumonic.

Pneumonia is the commonest cause of ninety nine
becoming louder in any area of the lung.

ANECDOTES

Did You Know That . . .

In the 20th Century there are only seven years whose numbers are a mathematical oddity because their numbers signify a prime number. The first one of its kind was the year 1951. The other six are 1973, 1979, 1987, 1993, 1997 and 1999.

□

If you were to count one number per second and counted seven hours per day, do you know how long it would take you to count to a billion? About 109 years.

□

The earth has existed for 2000000000 years. Scientists have worked it out, though approximately.

□

It is estimated that the width of the human hair is $\frac{3}{1000}$ inch. Do you know how many hairs placed side by side would measure an inch?

About 330

□

Scientists have worked out, though approximately, that life on earth has existed . . . 300000000 years.

□

Human life has existed on earth, scientists have worked out, though approximately . . . 300,000 years.

□

The distance between the earth and sun is about 150,000,000 Kilometres.

□

The cubic inch of average human blood is said to contain eighty thousand red corpuscles. If an average adult has 210 cubic inches blood, do you know how many red corpuscles are there in the body of an adult?

About 17000000000000 corpuscles.

□

The surface area of the globe, counting all continents and oceans is about 500 million kilometres.

□

The 'Cipher' means zero. The word 'Cipher', comes from the Arabic 'Sifr' and our word zero is derived from this word.

The red corpuscles in the human body is said to have the thickness of 00008 inch. Do you know approximately how high would all the corpuscles in an average adult's body be if they could be piled on top of one another without compression?

About 110,000,000 feet.

□

Supposing you had five billion pounds and you gave away a £500 note every minute, do you know how long it would take to give all your money away? Approximately 19 years.

□

Frank A Lone of New York denies that the decimal expansion of pi is 3.14159 . . . as is widely believed. He has computed more accurately by squaring pi, multiplying the result by 6, then dividing by 5 to get 3.14164078644620550.

□

Many centuries even before the birth of Christ the ancient Egyptians had attained a high degree of civilization. Among their various accomplishments was a form of picture writing known as *hieroglyphics*. Included in this, to satisfy their number requirements, was a set of numerical symbols.

□

It is believed that the Hindu-Arabic symbols

for numbers has been used as early as five or six
centuries before the birth of Christ. In the earliest
stages, however the Hindu-Arabic system of number
notation did not contain a symbol for zero. Without the zero the system was not of very much use.
The earliest known use of the Hindu-Arabic zero
occurs in an Indian inscription dated 876 A.D.
And the indisputable superiority of the Hindu-
Arabic system over all others is a consequence of
introducing the zero concept and symbol.

□

Zero is the only natural number that can be
added to any natural number to yield a sum that
is the same as the second natural number.

□

Our present system of *rod* measurement originated in sixteenth century Germany where the following rule served to establish the length and relationship between the foot and rod :

'If you stand at the door of a church on a Sunday,
and have sixteenth men stop-tall ones and short ones
—as they leave after service, and have them stand
so that their left feet are toe to heel behind each
other, the length obtained shall be the right and
lawful *rod* with which to measure sure and survey
land. Furthermore, the sixteenth part of that
distance shall be the right and lawful foot'

The inch came to us from the *Unica* which in Roman parlance was the twelfth part of some whole. Thus the inch is till today, the twelfth part of the foot.

☐

Recorded history of mathematics, in India, goes as far as 600 B.C. In this era Lord Buddha preached his spiritual message and also initiated a tradition in mathematics by his own work in arithmetic. It is stated in the Buddhist sacred book *Lalitavistara* that when Buddha was of the age to marry, he desired to marry Gopa. Gopa had over 500 other suitors. Therefore her father decided to hold an examination for all the suitors including Buddha, in order to select a worthy bridegroom for his daughter.

The subjects of the examinations included Arithmetic, Music and Archery. Buddha easily vanquished all his rivals except the great mathematician Arjuna. Buddha was matched against him and challenged to demonstrate his scientific skill.

In order to gain a victory over Arjuna, Buddha selected a very complicated operation in Arithmetic. He proceeded on to describe the number of 'Primary Atoms' which placed end to end, would form a line with length equal to the Ancient Hindu equivalent to a mile. He recited 'seven Primary Atoms make a very minute grain of dust. Seven of these grains of dust whirled up by the wind . . .' He

105

continued. When he reached the length of a mile, all the 7's listed by Buddha yielded a product of about 50 digits.

□

The greatest of the ancient Hindu mathematicians is reputed to be Bhaskaracharya. He was also famous as a poet and a philosopher. Bhaskaracharya's *Lilavati*, a treatise on mathematics is an immortal book—considered to be the greatest contribution ever made to the science of mathematics by a Hindu.

How the treatise of Bhaskaracharya *Lilavati* derived its name has an interesting story behind it!

Lilavati, in actual fact was the name of Bhaskaracharya's daughter. His only daughter. When she was born, two well-known astrologers had cast her horoscope. They had predicted that the stars under which Lilavati was born, were not favourable for her to lead a married life. And therefore they advised Bhaskaracharya not to get his daughter married. This was a great shock to Bhaskaracharya, as Lilavati was his only daughter. Therefore he pleaded with the Astrologers to calculate at least one auspicious moment, when the stars would favour her marriage.

Four days the astrologers calculated and came out with the auspicious moment—one and only auspicious moment!

When Lilavati reached her twelfth year, Bhaskara-charya arranged her marriage with a friend's son in a nearby village.

On the date set for the wedding, the bridegroom's party arrived in the hall, in a procession, and Lilavati was seated in the embrace of her uncle, who was to give away the bride. A screen was barring the first glimpse from her bridegroom.

To determine the exact moment, when the ceremony could start, the astrologers and priests set an hour glass besides Lilavati. Lilavati leaned over and gazed at the floating cup from time to time, to see how near she was approaching the propitious moment.

After quite some time had past, one of the astrologers looked into the hour glass and cried 'Alas the propitious moment has come and gone'! He lifted the vessel from the water. No liquid had entered the vessel and therefore no liquid had flown through the cavity.

As Lilavati sitting in the embrace of her uncle, in her anxiety, had bent several times over the cup, a pearl had dropped from her ornaments and blocked the opening through which the fluid should have passed. And now the auspicious hour had gone unnoticed and it was forever too late!

To console the unhappy Lilavati, to whom normal

pleasures of married life was denied forever, Bhaskaracharya, a man of great wisdom promised to work upon a book in mathematics and name it after her!

Through years of labouring he created the book that has brought immortal fame to Lilavati. And the world is richer by the great work!

The following is a well-known problem from *Lilavati* :

'A necklace was broken during an amorous struggle. One-third of the pearls fell to the ground, one-fifth stayed on the couch, one-sixth was found by the girl, and one-tenth recovered by her lover; six pearls remained on the string. Say of how many pearls the necklace was composed.'

Here is another one :

'Beautiful maiden with beaming eyes, tell me which is the number that, multiplied by 3, then increased by three-fourths of the product, divided by 7, diminished by 1/3rd of the quotient, multiplied by itself diminished by 52, the square root found, addition of 8, division by 10 gives the number 2?'

□

The over-anxiety on the part of Brahmins—the scholarly caste—in India to keep the knowledge a secret from their bretheren of the other castes and

108

various feuds and family wars made them resort to the use of a secret code known as the Sutras. Thus the secret coded Sutras in mathematics and other allied scientific literature took shape. While it was helpful in making the study of the various sciences simpler, precise and more standardised, it was impossible for even the most learned scholars to interpret the literature—unless someone decodified the sutras. While the Brahmins could protect the treasure of their knowledge from others, knowledge got locked in the hands of a few experts who possessed the keys for decodification. Thus various valuable science, art and literature remained miles away from the common man.

The following is a hymn, an example of codified knowledge in mathematics:

Gopi Bhagyamaduv rata Shringishodadi Sandiga
Kala Jeevitarava Tava Galaddhalara Sangara

The above Sanskrit hymn is meant as a praise to Lord Krishna. And it would be very difficult for one to imagine the hidden meaning in it. But when decodified, it gives the value of Pi (π) to 30 places of decimals.

□

Pythogoras not only thought of numbers in his mind, but he also felt the numbers in his heart. He was emotionally attached to numbers. They were more just symbols for him. He saw life in them. He

109

often expressed his feeling for numbers in poetic fashion. He heard the 'Music of Spheres'. He saw in the cardinal integers 'Images of Creativeness'. He invested the numbers with various properties. This is the way he explained them:

ONE: Stood apart as the source of all numbers and represented reason.

TWO: Stood for man

THREE: For women

FOUR: Stood for justice, since it is the product of equals.

FIVE: Represented marriage, since it is formed by the union of two and three.

□

During the reign of King Ptolemy (300 B.C.) Euclid founded a School in Alexandria. He also taught in his own school. The textbook he wrote on mathematics 'Elements' became a great asset in the world of mathematics.

There is an interesting story. King Ptolemy once asked him if there is a short cut to Geometry than that of the elements. Euclid replied, 'There is no royal road to Geometry'. Another interesting story concerns him and his pupils. After learning the very first proposition in Geometry, the pupil asked him what will he gain by learning these things. Euclid

110

called his slave and said 'Give him three pence since he must need make gains by what he learns'.

Euclid's great work 'Elements' contains 13 volumes and his textbook has remained in use almost unchanged for more than 2000 years.

☐

Hypatia (410 A.D.) enjoys the place of being the first woman mathematician in recorded history. Her special work in mathematics includes commentaries on the work of Diophantes, particularly Diophontine Algebra.

She became the head of the Neoplatonic School in Alexandria. The lectures she delivered in the capacity of the Head of the Alexandria School attracted distinguished men from all over the continent. Unfortunately her glorious life came to an unhappy ending. A group of fanatical mob of anti-pagans attacked and brutally slashed her to death with oystershells and burnt her piecemeal.

All her scientific writings were lost.

☐

Everyone knows that Omar Khayyam was the author of immortal *Rubaiyat* but few are acquainted with the fact that he was a great mathematician and astronomer of his time, and the most original of all the Saracen mathematicians. He devised a calendar superior to the one we use. His work in the field of

Algebra was the greatest contribution to the subject between the fifth and fourteenth centuries. Here is a stanza of his regarding his calendar.

'Ah but my computations, people say,
Reduce the year to better reckoning-hay
'Tis only striking from the calendar
Unborn tomorrow and dead yesterday.'

☐

Rene Descartes, who enjoys the distinction of being called 'Father of Modern Mathematics' was a versatile man who had creative instincts in other fields as well such as—Philosophy, Physics, Cosmology, Chemistry, Physiology and Psychology. The mathematical family, which Rene Descartes initiated Analytical Geometry became exceedingly prolific in the future days.

Rene Descartes's father, a very rich French gentleman expected his son also to lead a leisurely life. And Rene was a weak child. He started his formal schooling only at the age of eight!

Having always been delicate in health, he developed the habit of spending most of his mornings lying around in bed. He did this particularly whenever he wished to think.

One such morning set a turning point in his life. On that morning he discovered Analytical Geometry. Lying on the bed his eyes caught a fly crawling on the ceiling of his room. He set himself the problem of describing the path of the fly in the language of mathematics, when the idea of analytical geometry came to his mind!

□

Issac Newton, often cited as the greatest genius, the human race has ever produced, was also famous for his absentmindedness. A very popular one relates that he cut two holes in his door, one for his cat and a little one for her kitten.

Another story goes that one evening, when he was entertaining his guests to dinner, he left the table to fetch a bottle of wine from the cellar. On his way to the cellar he completely forgot where he was going. Then he straight went to his room, donned the surplice and appeared in his chapel.

Of all the stories about Newton's forgetfulness the most interesting one is about him and a Miss Storey, step-daughter of a Mr Clarke, the village apothecary, with whom Newton was lodging. At that time he was nineteen and attending the Grammar School. He is said to have fallen in love with Miss Storey and had become engaged to her. But after sometime he forgot all about it. Although he remembered his fancy for her, throughout his life, he never could recall the promise he had made to her, to marry her.

113

Miss Storey had to marry a lesser genius and console herself.

☐

Albert Einstein, one of the greatest figures of the world, in Mathematics and Physics was well-known for his simple ways and unassuming nature. There are many stories told about his simplicity by the people who lived in his neighbourhood in Princeton. The most popular story is the one about him and a little girl who lived in his neighbourhood.

It is said that the little girl's mother noticed that the child often went to Einstein's house. The mother wondered about this and questioned her daughter. The child replied 'I had trouble with my home work in Arithmetic. People said that at No. 112 there lives a very big mathematician, who is also a very good man. I went to him and asked him to help me with my homework. He was willing and explained everything very well. It was easier to understand than when our teacher explained it in school. He said I should come whenever I find a problem too difficult'. The child's mother was panic-stricken, and rushed to Einstein's house to apologise for her daughter's behaviour. But Einstein said 'You don't have to excuse yourself. I have certainly learned more from the conversation with the child, than she did from me'.

☐

Ramanujan, the great Indian mathematician

began correspondence with G. H. Hardy, the Fellow of Trinity College. His first letter to Hardy, dated January 16, 1913 goes as follows:

"Dear Sir,

"I beg to introduce myself to you as a clerk in the Accounts Department of the Port Trust Office at Madras on a salary of only $ 20 per annum. I am now about 23 years of age. I have had no University education but I have undergone the ordinary school course. After leaving school I have been employing the spare time at my disposal to work at Mathematics. I have not trodden through the conventional regular course which is followed in a University course, but I am striking out a new path for myself. I have made a special investigation of divergent series in general and the results I get are termed by the local mathematicians as 'startling' . . .

I would request you to go through the enclosed papers. Being poor, if you are convinced that there is anything of value I would like to have my theorems published. I have not given the actual investigations nor the expressions that I get but I have indicated the lines on which I proceed. Being inexperienced I would very highly value any advice you give me. Requesting to be excused for the trouble I give you.

I remain, Dear Sir, Yours truly,

S. RAMANUJAN

To the letter attached was 120 theorems.

Ramanujan used to say that goddess Namagiri the goodess of Namakkal inspired him with the formulae in dreams. It is a remarkable fact that on rising from bed he would frequently note down results and verify them. This pattern repeated itself throughout his life.

☐

Everyone knows Lewis Carroll as the creator of the immortal *Alice in Wonderland* but very few people know him also as a mathematician. His pen name was derived by translating his given name Charles Lutwidge into Latin -- Carulos Ludovicus -- and then reversing and anglicizing the result.

He was a mathematics teacher and a writer on mathematical subject. The subject which interested him most was that of the logical foundations of mathematics. He also possessed rare mathematical insight.

His dual personality gave rise to many legends, and one story claims that Queen Victoria delighted with *Alice in Wonderland*, ordered that Carroll's next book be delivered to her as soon as released. She was somewhat taken aback to receive *The Elements of Determinants (with their application to simultaneous Linear Equations and Algebraical Geometry)*.

☐

The Indian Mathematician Sessa, the inventor of the game of Chess, was ordered by the King of Persia to ask a recompense whatever he might wish. Sessa modestly requested to be given one grain of wheat for the first square of the board, two for the second, four for the third, and so on doubling each time upto the sixty fourth square. The wise men of the King added the numbers 1, 2, 4, 8, 16, 32, 64 etc and found the sum of the series to sixty-four terms to be 18446744073709551615 grains of wheat. Taking 9000 grains in a pint we find the whole number of bushels to be over 320000000000 00, which is several times the annual wheat production of the whole world.

□

Julius Caesar, with the help of the astronomer Siosenejes, introduced the method of reckoning known as the Julian Calendar. The year being 365.2422 Solar days, he took 365 such days for a common year and 366 days for a leap year, so that the average length of a year was 365.25 days. In the Julian Calendar all years divisible by 4 were leap years, and in the Gregorian calendar, years divisible by 4 are leap years unless they are divisible by 100 and not 400. Thus, in the Gregorian calendar the years 1600 and 2000 are leap years but the years 1700, 1800 and 1900 are common years. In 1582 the Julian calendar was ten days slower than the Gregorian, after 1700 it became 11 days slower and since 1900 it has been thirteen days slower. Hence January 1, 1917 of the Gregorian calendar corresponds to December 19, 1916 of the Julian.

117

In Great Britain the change of the Julian to the Gregorian calendar was not made until 1752. In September of that year eleven days were omitted from the almanacs.

□

What are the chances of your winning the big prize if you buy one of the 5,000,000 tickets of the sweepstakes? Just about one in 4000,000

What are your chances in winning in Roulette? Thirtysix times the amount wagered is about one in 36.

What are the chances of your getting thirteen cards of the same suit in Bridge? About 1 in 153,000,000 000.

What is your chance of getting a straight flush in Poker.? About one in 62000. Four of a kind about one in 4000. A full house about one in 600. Three of a kind, about one in 50. Two pairs about one in 20.

□

When Pythogoras was walking home one day, he was passing through a blacksmiths' shop. He stopped with delight when he heard the ring of the hammers on the anvils make a harmonious sound.

Five blacksmiths were at work and as it happened they were all using different sized hammers. Pythogoras was fascinated by the sound made by the hammers which was like a musical chime. He soon realised that because each hammer was of a different weight each had a different ring when it hit the anvil. And the heavier the hammer the lower the note it made.

However he also realised that there was one hammer which was spoiling the harmony of the sound.

Pythogoras requested the blacksmiths to let him try some experiments with their hammers. They agreed.

He weighed each hammer in turn and found that the hammer that spoilt the chime had a weight which did not fit into a simple order of numbers. With further experiments, Pythagoras soon learnt how to make a musical scale using different sized hammers. This is one of the earliest and greatest discoveries in music.

TABLES
FOR
READY
REFERENCE

MULTIPLICATION TABLE

×	0	1	2	3	4	5	6	7	8	9	10	11	12
0	0	0	0	0	0	0	0	0	0	0	0	0	0
1	0	1	2	3	4	5	6	7	8	9	10	11	12
2	0	2	4	6	8	10	12	14	16	18	20	22	24
3	0	3	6	9	12	15	18	21	24	27	30	33	36
4	0	4	8	12	16	20	24	28	32	36	40	44	48
5	0	5	10	15	20	25	30	35	40	45	50	55	60
6	0	6	12	18	24	30	36	42	48	54	60	66	72
7	0	7	14	21	28	35	42	49	56	63	70	77	84
8	0	8	16	24	32	40	48	56	64	72	80	88	96
9	0	9	18	27	36	45	54	63	72	81	90	99	108
10	0	10	20	30	40	50	60	70	80	90	100	110	120
11	0	11	22	33	44	55	66	77	88	99	110	121	132
12	0	12	24	36	48	60	72	84	96	108	120	132	144

To divide by	Simply
10, 100, 1000, etc.	move decimal point **one**, two, three, etc. places to the *left* in dividend.
0.1, 0.01, 0.001, etc.	move decimal point **one, two,** three, etc. places to **the *right*** in dividend.
$3\frac{1}{3}$	multiply by 3 and divide **by 10.**
$33\frac{1}{3}$	multiply by 3 and divide **by 100.**
$333\frac{1}{3}$	multiply by 3 and divide **by 1000.**
$16\frac{2}{3}$	multiply by 6 and divide **by 100.**
$12\frac{1}{2}$	multiply by 8 and divide **by 100**
$8\frac{1}{3}$	multiply by 12 **and divide by** 100.
25	multiply by 4 and divide **by** 100.
50	multiply by 2 and divide **by** 100.
125	multiply **by 8 and divide by** 1000.

To multiply by	Simply
10, 100, 1000, etc.	move decimal point one, two, three, etc. places to the *right* in multiplicand.
0.1, 0.01, 0.001, etc.	move decimal point one, two, three, etc. places to the *left* in multiplicand.
5, 50, 500, etc.	multiply by 10, 100, 1000, etc. and divide by 2
25, 250, etc.	multiply by 100, 1000, etc. and divide by 4.
125	multiply by 1000 and divide by 8.
$33\frac{1}{3}$, $16\frac{2}{3}$, $12\frac{1}{2}$, $8\frac{1}{3}$, $6\frac{1}{4}$	multiply by 100 and divide by 3, 6, 8, 12, 16.

A number is divisible by	if
2	last figure is 0 or one divisible by 2.
3	sum of its digits is divisible by 3.
4	number represented by last two digits is divisible by 4 or both are zeros.
5	last digit is 0 or 5.
6	it is an even number the sum of whose digits is divisible by 3.
7	(no known rule)
8	number represented by last three digits is divisible by 8.
9	sum of its digits is divisible by 9.

DECIMAL EQUIVALENTS OF COMMON FRACTIONS

$\frac{1}{64}$ = .015625	$\frac{11}{32}$ = .34375	$\frac{11}{16}$ = .6875
$\frac{1}{32}$ = .03125	$\frac{3}{8}$ = .375	$\frac{23}{32}$ = .71875
$\frac{1}{16}$ = .0625	$\frac{13}{32}$ = .40625	$\frac{3}{4}$ = .75
$\frac{3}{32}$ = .09375	$\frac{7}{16}$ = .4375	$\frac{25}{32}$ = .78125
$\frac{1}{8}$ = .125	$\frac{15}{32}$ = .46875	$\frac{13}{16}$ = .8125
$\frac{5}{32}$ = .15625	$\frac{1}{2}$ = .5	$\frac{27}{32}$ = .84375
$\frac{3}{16}$ = .1875	$\frac{17}{32}$ = .53125	$\frac{7}{8}$ = .875
$\frac{7}{32}$ = .21875	$\frac{9}{16}$ = .5625	$\frac{29}{32}$ = .90625
$\frac{1}{4}$ = .25	$\frac{19}{32}$ = .59375	$\frac{15}{16}$ = .9375
$\frac{9}{32}$ = .28125	$\frac{5}{8}$ = .625	$\frac{31}{32}$ = .96875
$\frac{5}{16}$ = .3125	$\frac{21}{32}$ = .65625	$\frac{63}{64}$ = .984375

PER CENTS AS FRACTIONS

5%	=	0.05	=	$\frac{1}{20}$	$33\frac{1}{3}\%$	=	$0.33\frac{1}{3}$	=	$\frac{1}{3}$	60%	=	0.60	=	$\frac{3}{5}$
$8\frac{1}{3}\%$	=	$0.08\frac{1}{3}$	=	$\frac{1}{12}$	$37\frac{1}{2}\%$	=	0.375	=	$\frac{3}{8}$	$62\frac{1}{2}\%$	=	0.625	=	$\frac{5}{8}$
$12\frac{1}{2}\%$	=	0.125	=	$\frac{1}{8}$	40%	=	0.40	=	$\frac{2}{5}$	75%	=	0.75	=	$\frac{3}{4}$
$16\frac{2}{3}\%$	=	$0.16\frac{2}{3}$	=	$\frac{1}{6}$	$41\frac{2}{3}\%$	=	$0.41\frac{2}{3}$	=	$\frac{5}{12}$	80%	=	0.80	=	$\frac{4}{5}$
20%	=	0.20	=	$\frac{1}{5}$	50%	=	0.50	=	$\frac{1}{2}$	$83\frac{1}{3}\%$	=	$0.83\frac{1}{3}$	=	$\frac{5}{6}$
25%	=	0.25	=	$\frac{1}{4}$	$58\frac{1}{3}\%$	=	$0.58\frac{1}{3}$	=	$\frac{7}{12}$	$87\frac{1}{2}\%$	=	0.875	=	$\frac{7}{8}$

MULTIPLES OF π

No.	Value	Log	No.	Value	Log
1	3.1416	0.4971	1	0.3183	9.5029 — 10
2	6.2832	0.7982	$\frac{1}{2}$	1.5708	0.1961
3	9.4248	0.9743	$\frac{1}{3}$	1.0472	0.0200
4	12.5664	1.0992	$\frac{1}{4}$	0.7854	9.8951 — 10
5	15.7080	1.1961	$\frac{1}{5}$	0.6283	9.7982 — 10
6	18.8496	1.2753	$\frac{1}{6}$	0.5236	9.7190 — 10
7	21.9912	1.3422	$\frac{1}{7}$	0.4488	9.6521 — 10
8	25.1328	1.4002	$\frac{1}{8}$	0.3927	9.5941 — 10
9	21.2744	1.4514	$\frac{1}{9}$	0.3491	9.5429 — 10
	9.8696	0.9943		1.7725	0.2486

(1) If the multiplier and the multiplicand have the same sign, the product is positive.

(2) If the multiplier and the multiplicand have opposite signs, the product is negative.

(3) If the dividend and the divisor have the same sign, the quotient is positive.

(4) If the dividend and the divisor have opposite signs, the quotient is negative.

FOR EASY MEMORIZATION

Multiplication	Division
$+ \times + = +$	$+ \div + = +$
$+ \times - = -$	$+ \div - = -$
$- \times + = -$	$- \div + = -$
$- \times - = +$	$- \div - = +$

ABOUT ZERO

(1) Any number plus zero equals the number.

(2) Any number minus zero equals the number.

(3) Zero minus any number equals the negative of the number.

(4) Any number times zero equals zero.

(5) Zero divided by any number except zero equals zero.

(6) The operation of dividing by zero is not defined and is not permitted.

Prefix	Abbreviation	Meaning
milli	m	denotes 0.001
centi	c	denotes 0.01
deci	d	denotes 0.1
deka	dk	denotes 10
hecto	h	denotes 100
kilo	k	denotes 1000

10 millimetres (mm) = 1 centimetre (cm) = 0.01 metre

10 centimetres = 1 decimetre (dm) = 0.1 metre

10 decimetres = 1 metre (m)

10 metres = 1 dekametre (dkm) = 10 metres

10 dekametres = 1 hectometre (hm) = 100 metres

10 hectometres = 1 kilometre (km) = 1000 metres

1 cubic decimetre equals 1 litre,

1 litre of water weighs 1 kilogram,

1 *are* is an area of 100 square metres.

Exponential Form	Logarithmic Form
. . . . .	. . . . .
$10^3 = 1000$	$\log 1000 = 3$
$10^2 = 100$	$\log 100 = 2$
$10^1 = 10$	$\log 10 = 1$
$10^0 = 1$	$\log 1 = 0$
$10^{-1} = 0.1$	$\log 0.1 = -1$
$10^{-2} = 0.01$	$\log 0.01 = -2$
$10^{-3} = 0.001$	$\log 0.001 = -3$
. . . . .	. . . . .

THE EARTH

Mean diameter $= 7912.464$

Surface area $= 1.967 \times 10^8$ square miles

Mass $= 1.3173 \times 10^{25}$ pounds

Mean distance from sun $= 92.9$ million miles

Velocity of escape $= 36,000$ ft. / sec.

Length of year in days $=$
$365.24219879 - 0.0000000614 \ (t-1900)$

$(t = \text{present year})$

Length of day $= 23$h. 56m. 04.09054s. of mean solar
time

MEASURES OF VOLUME

1728 cubic inches (cu. in.)   1 = cubic foot (cu. ft.)

27 cubic feet   1 = cubic yard (cu. yd.)

128 cubic feet   = 1 cord (cd.)

LIQUID MEASURES

4 gills (gi.) = 1 pint (pt.) = 16 fluid ounces

2 pints   = 1 quart (qt.)

4 quarts   = 1 gallon (gal)=231 cubic inches

$31\frac{1}{2}$ gals.   = 1 barrel (bbl.)

DRY MEASURES

2 pints   = 1 quart (qt.)

8 quarts   = 1 peck (pk.)

4 pecks   = 1 bushel (bu.) = 2150.42
                                cubic inches

MEASURE OF TIME

60 seconds (sec.)	=	1 minute (min.)
60 minutes	=	1 hour (hr.)
24 hours	=	1 day (da.)
7 days	=	1 week (wk.)
365 days	=	1 common year (yr.)
366 days	=	1 leap year
1 lunar month (mo.)	=	29 days, 12 hours, 44 minutes

MEASURES OF LENGTH

12 inches (in.)	=	1 foot (ft.)
3 feet (ft.)	=	1 yard (yd.)
$16\frac{1}{2}$ feet (ft.)	=	1 rod (rd.)

320 rods = 1760 yards = 5280 feet = 1 mile

MEASURE OF AREA

144 square inches (in.^{2}) = 1 square foot (sq. ft.)

9 square feet   (ft.^{2}) = 1 square yard (sq. yd.)

$30\frac{1}{4}$ square yards (yd.^{2}) = 1 square rod (sq. rd.)

160 square rods (rd.^{2}) = 1 acre (A.)

640 acres   = 1 square mile (sq. mi.)

AVOIRDUPOIS WEIGHTS

16 drams (dr.)   = 1 ounce (oz.)

/000 grains (gr.)   = 1 pound (lb.)

16 ounces (oz.)   = 1 pound

100 pounds   = 1 hundredweight (cwt.)

2000 pounds   = 1 ton (T.)

2240 pounds   = 1 long ton

TROY WEIGHTS

24 grains	= 1 pennyweight (pwt.)
20 pennyweights	= 1 ounce (oz.)
12 ounces	= 1 pound
5760 grains	= 1 pound
3.168 grains	= 1 carat

APOTHECARIES' WEIGHTS

20 grains	= 1 scruple
3 scruples	= 1 dram
8 drams	= 1 ounce

1 cubic decimetre equals 1 litre,

1 litre of water weighs 1 kilogram,

1 *are* is an area of 100 square metres.

LENGTHS

To change from	to	Multiply by
inches	cm.	2.540005
feet	cm.	30.48006
yards	m.	0.914402
miles	km.	1.60935
centimetres	in.	0.3937
metres	ft.	3.28083
kilometres	m:.	0.621372

AREAS

sq.in	sq.cm.	6.451626
sq.ft.	sq.m.	0.0929034
sq.yds.	sq.m.	0.8361307
acres	ares	40.46873
sq.mi.	sq.km.	2.589998
sq.cm.	sq.in.	0.155
sq.m.	sq.ft.	10.76387
sq.km.	sq.mi.	0.3861006

VOLUMES

To change from	to	Multiply by
cu.in.	cc.	16.38716
cu.ft.	cu.m.	0.028317
cu.yd.	cu.m.	0.764559
cu.m.	cu.ft.	35.3144
cu.m.	cu.yd.	1.30794

CAPACITY — LIQUID

ounces	cc.	29.57
pints	litres	0.473167
quarts	litres	0.946333
gallons	litres	3.785332
litres	fl.oz.	33.8174
litres	qts.	1.05671
litres	gal.	0.264178
cc.	ounces	0.033815

CAPACITY — DRY

To change from	to	Multiply by
pints	litres	0.550599
quarts	litres	1.101198
pecks	litres	8.80958
bushels	litres	35.2383
litres	pints	1.81620
litres	qts.	0.908102
dekalitres	pecks	1.13513
hectolitres	bu.	2.83782

WEIGHTS (AVOIRDUPOIS)

grains	grams	0.0647989
ounces	grams	28.349527
pounds	kg.	0.4535924
tons	kg.	907.18486
grams	grains	15.43235639
kilograms	lbs.	2.2046223
metric tons	lbs.	2204.6223

TABLE OF DAYS BETWEEN TWO DATES

Day	Jan.	Feb.	March	April	May	June	July	Aug.	Sept.	Oct.	Nov	Dec.
1	1	32	60	91	121	152	182	213	244	274	305	335
2	2	33	61	92	122	153	183	214	245	275	306	336
3	3	34	62	93	123	154	184	215	246	276	307	337
4	4	35	63	94	124	155	185	216	247	277	308	338
5	5	36	64	95	125	156	186	217	248	278	309	339
6	6	37	65	96	126	157	187	218	249	279	310	340
7	7	38	66	97	127	158	188	219	250	280	311	341
8	8	39	67	98	128	159	189	220	251	281	312	342
9	9	40	68	99	129	160	190	221	252	282	313	343
10	10	41	69	100	130	161	191	222	253	283	314	344

11	11	42	70	101	131	162	192	223	254	284	315	345
12	12	43	71	102	132	163	193	224	255	285	316	346
13	13	44	72	103	133	164	194	225	256	286	317	347
14	14	45	73	104	134	165	195	226	257	287	318	348
15	15	46	74	105	135	166	196	227	258	288	319	349
16	16	47	75	106	136	167	197	228	259	289	320	350
17	17	48	76	107	137	168	198	229	260	290	321	351
18	18	49	77	108	138	169	199	230	261	291	322	352
19	19	50	78	109	139	170	200	231	262	292	323	353
20	20	51	79	110	140	171	201	232	263	293	324	354
21	21	52	80	111	141	172	202	233	264	294	325	355
22	22	53	81	112	142	173	203	234	265	295	326	356
23	23	54	82	113	143	174	204	235	266	296	327	357
24	24	55	83	114	144	175	205	236	267	297	328	358
25	25	56	84	115	145	176	206	237	268	298	329	359

26	26	57	85	116	146	177	207	238	269	299	330	360
27	27	58	86	117	147	178	208	239	270	300	331	361
28	28	59	87	118	148	179	209	240	271	301	332	362
29	29	...	88	119	149	180	210	241	272	302	333	363
30	30	...	89	120	150	181	211	242	273	303	334	364
31	31	...	90	...	151	...	212	243	...	304	...	365

For Leap Year, one day must be added to each number of days after February 28.

Dear Reader,

Welcome to the world of **Orient Paperbacks**—India's largest selling paperbacks in English. We hope you have enjoyed reading this book and would want to know more about **Orient Paperbacks.**

There are more than 400 **Orient Paperbacks** on a variety of subjects to entertain and inform you. The list of authors published in **Orient Paperbacks** includes, amongst others, distinguished and well-known names as Dr. S. Radhakrishna.ı, R.K. Narayan, Raja Rao, Manohar Malgonkar, Khushwant Singh, Anita Desai, Kamala Das, Dr. O.P. Jaggi, H.K. Bakhru, Norman Vincent Peale, Sasthi Brata and Dr. Promilla Kapur. **Orient Paperbacks** truly represent the best of Indian writing in English today.

We would be happy to keep you continuously informed of the new titles and programmes of **Orient Paperbacks** through our monthly newsletter, **Orient Literary Review.** Send in your name and full address to us today. We will start sending you **Orient Literary Review** completely free of cost.

Available at all bookshops or by V.P.P.

Orient Paperbacks
Madarsa Road, Kashmere Gate, Delhi-110 006